WILDLIFE AFTER GRAVEL

Twenty Years of Practical Research by The Game Conservancy and ARC

NICK GILES
WETLANDS RESEARCH UNIT
THE GAME CONSERVANCY

The research described in this book, and the publication of the results, have been fully funded by ARC Ltd.

Published by
Game Conservancy Limited
Fordingbridge
Hampshire
SP6 1EF, UK

Printed and bound in Great Britain by BAS Printers Ltd

Page make-up/typesetting by
McKenzie Clark Creative Agency

Front cover: Wildlife After Gravel by Chris Orgill

Vignettes: The vignettes used throughout the book
were kindly made available by the following artists:

Jonathan Yule   pages 27,33,47,71,74,110,119
Rodger McPhail   pages 13,15,23,35,50,125
Guy Troughton   pages 38,95,108
Malcolm Kaye   page   101
Chris Orgill   page   61

ISBN 0 9500130 3 X

CONTENTS

Authorship and Acknowledgements

The Introduction and Chapters 1,2,6 and 8 were written by Nick Giles, Head of the Game Conservancy's Wetland Research Unit. Chapters 4 and 7 are by Vivien Phillips and Chapters 3 and 5 by John Phillips. Helen Giles abstracted and collated the scientific papers and articles written by staff of the research project. Lorraine Josling typed the text and Jo France assisted Nick Giles with the computer graphics. Judy Pittock incorporated the late changes and Charles Nodder supervised the publication. The Game Conservancy's research team would like to thank ARC Ltd for their constant support, encouragement and advice.

FOREWORD

Conservation of the environment is most important for the future of the countryside and as a major aggregate producer with significant land resources, ARC Ltd has always taken very seriously its responsibilities to the countryside. We have proved that the partnership between aggregate producer and conservationist can be very productive.

It is a testimony to our commitment that our research partnership with The Game Conservancy is twenty years old and the ARC Wildfowl Centre has become recognised for the high quality of its research and is an outstanding wildlife reserve in its own right. The future of the reserve at Great Linford is secure and the lessons in wildlife ecology learned there will endure for all time.

The Game Conservancy is to be congratulated on its work over these years. Its research has established the complex interrelationship between insects, fish and waterfowl and, to the benefit of all wildlife, has been able to provide valuable tested techniques for the management of man-made inland waters.

I am sure you will find the contents of this book valuable and informative.

THE LORD HANSON
October 1992

INTRODUCTION

The creation of new wetlands through industrial activity is increasingly important as natural wetlands decline

The conservation of wetlands

Over recent centuries, natural habitat loss in the British Isles, and indeed worldwide, has been very extensive and damaging to wildlife. Wetlands such as rivers, streams, estuaries, salt marshes, bogs and lakes have all suffered. The great biological species diversity which natural wetlands support makes them especially worth conserving. At the same time, industrial activity gives us a rare opportunity to create completely new wetland habitats for wildlife.

Sand and gravel extraction is essential for the buildings and roads on which we depend.

We clearly need an adequate supply of building materials for the future. By excavating sand and gravel quarries, the aggregates industry creates around 400 to 500 hectares of new lakes each year in the UK. The total UK area of flooded disused sand and gravel quarries is now around 15 000 hectares. The potential after uses of this resource are many and can range from intensive activities such as coarse fishing, put-and-take trout angling, scuba diving, sailing and water ski-ing, through to carefully managed nature reserves.

In suburban sites where green areas are scarce, well restored mineral operations can provide excellent quality amenity and conservation areas. However, a good understanding of the ecology of such habitats is crucial for correct restoration procedures. It is a fallacy to suppose that simply allowing mineral workings to flood after excavation has finished will allow nature to take over and produce a high quality wildlife reserve. With no human intervention, common and widespread species will invade and establish a species-poor system, dominated often by willow and alder trees around the lake edges, with common aquatic weeds filling in most areas of water. Quality wildlife habitats need to be carefully created and managed. Only applied practical research can provide the vital information necessary for conservationists, planners and developers.

1

Abandoning worked out gravel pits 'to nature' will lead only to low quality habitats. A complete restoration plan is essential to maximising the conservation potential.

The start of the Wildfowl Project

In the spring of 1970 ARC management personnel visited The Game Conservancy's headquarters at Fordingbridge, Hampshire, to seek ways in which ARC could make a significant contribution to wildlife conservation and accelerate the natural colonisation of disused sand and gravel works. Prior to this meeting The Game Conservancy's Nigel Gray had carried out trials on a small gravel pit near Fordingbridge, discovering in the process the characteristic poor duckling survival which wildfowl tend to experience on these waters, with the attendant lack of sporting potential. ARC and The Game Conservancy surveyed a number of potential study sites before proposals were drawn up for a joint scheme, leading to the establishment of the Wildfowl Research Project at Great Linford in Buckinghamshire. Nigel Gray was helped considerably in his choice of the site by the late Dr Jeffrey Harrison of WAGBI (Wildfowlers Association of Great Britain and Ireland, now BASC, the British Association for Shooting and Conservation).

It was agreed at the outset of the Wildfowl Project that the ultimate objective was to learn how to restore and manage gravel pits so that they could become highly productive for wildfowl, particularly ducks. Both Nigel Gray and ARC's Rudolf Agnew wanted the ARC sponsorship to provide core funding for applied ecological research to answer the following questions:

(1)   How should gravel pits be physically structured for wildfowl conservation?

(2)   How should they be planted to create a diverse, productive botanical community?

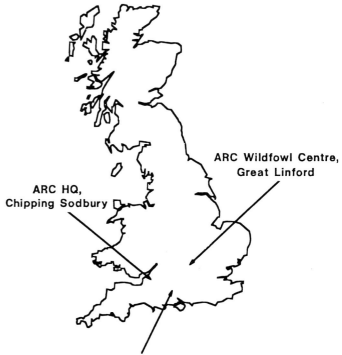

ARC HQ, Chipping Sodbury

ARC Wildfowl Centre, Great Linford

Game Conservancy, Fordingbridge

The Great Linford study site was chosen with care and is within reasonably convenient range of the headquarters of both parent bodies.

(3)   How should the developing ecosystem be managed to produce the best possible conditions for duck breeding, with special reference to the supply of insect food for ducklings?

For the first 10 years or so of its operation The Game Conservancy's Wildfowl Research Project was housed in a small site office at Great Linford. In 1980 ARC decided to construct the purpose built Wildfowl Centre which is still in active use at the site today. This report embodies a digest of the key information resulting from the research at Great Linford over the past 20

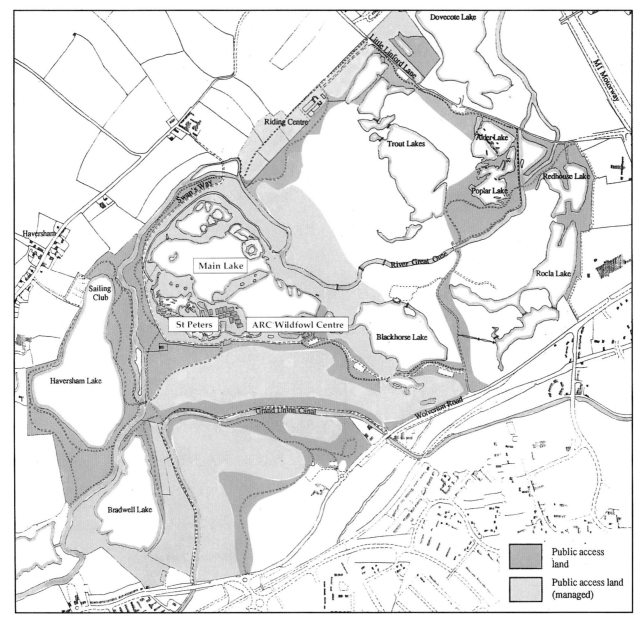

The worked out gravel pits at Great Linford are strung out along the flood plain of the River Great Ouse and have been restored to a variety of conservation and recreation needs. The Wildfowl Reserve lakes, Main Lake and St Peters, are in the centre of the group.

years. We hope that it will serve both as a record of the scientific achievement and as a useful practical handbook for those wishing to restore gravel pits to high quality wildlife habitat.

The fact that more than 30% of breeding wildfowl and over 25% of the wintering waterfowl populations of several UK species are found on gravel pits makes these sites vitally important as bird conservation habitats and bird watching sites for Britain's ornithologists. In 1980 a Wildfowl and Wetlands Trust survey of breeding waterfowl on inland UK waters found that the following species had 10% of more of their numbers based on gravel pits: mallard, pochard, tufted duck, mute swan, Canada goose, moorhen, coot, great crested grebe and dabchick. Of wintering species over the same period the following had 10% or more

of their inland maximum population counts on gravel pits: mallard, gadwall, shoveler, pochard, tufted duck, goosander, mute swan and Canada goose. The research at Great Linford has shown us exactly why worked out gravel pits have become so important to wildfowl and other wildlife. It has also shown us the best ways to maximise the conservation benefits of restored gravel pits where nature conservation is selected as the chosen after use.

It is worth remembering that the initial challenge for the Game Conservancy ecologists 20 years ago was a considerable one: How do you turn the relative biological desert left after mineral extraction has finished into a high quality wildlife conservation area tailored specifically to the requirements of breeding ducks? Over the 20 years of collaboration, The Game

The Game Conservancy's original wildfowl laboratory was housed in a small site office.

The partnership began in 1970 with the establishment of the wildfowl sanctuary on worked out gravel pits at Great Linford.

Conservancy and ARC have answered this question and achieved their joint goals. Today the Great Linford Wildfowl Reserve is nationally important for the conservation of a number of species. It is also regarded as one of the best bird watching sites in Buckinghamshire. The initial breeding community of ducks was limited to just two – mallard and tufted duck – whereas today at Great Linford we have mallard, tufted, pochard, gadwall, shoveler and the exotic ruddy duck all attempting to nest within the confines of the reserve.

But the research over the duration of the project has extended well beyond its original aims in relation to wildfowl productivity. The chapters of this book and the list of scientific and other papers published as a result of the research at Great Linford (see Appendix 1) testify to the diversity of wildlife which can make use of gravel pits when they have been correctly restored. We hope that the book will act as a stimulus to others who want to mirror the success of the Great Linford story.

The present ARC Wildfowl Centre, managed by The Game Conservancy, was built in 1970 and opened by Michael Heseltine MP, then Minister of State for the Environment.

Management Guidelines

Key findings of significance to gravel pit reserve managers are highlighted in boxes in the forthcoming chapters so that they can be readily found in the text.

RESEARCH SUMMARY

The following paragraphs detail the chronology 1971-1992 of the key research findings from The Game Conservancy's Wildfowl Research Project.

● During the 1960s mallard duckling mortality on gravel pits near Fordingbridge was found to be high, with few ducklings surviving to fledging (Gray, 1974). Comparisons with Dutch research suggested a shortage of insects was to blame.

Only rarely did many ducklings survive on abandoned gravel pits. A brood of young mallard outside a nest box on a raft.

● In 1973, Lees & Street described the early diet of downy mallard and tufted ducklings, comparing it with the food available to the birds on gravel pits. Very young mallard ate largely aquatic insects (especially chironomid midges), whilst older mallard ducklings switched to a largely vegetarian diet. Tufted ducklings ate aquatic snails, especially *Potamopyrgus jenkinsii*, an abundant species in newly maturing gravel pits.

● The key importance of an adequate (protein-rich) insect diet for young mallard was subsequently demonstrated with laboratory feeding trials (Street, 1978).

● Analyses of the diet of older mallard (Street, 1975) showed that adult birds also eat a high proportion of aquatic invertebrates in their spring and summer diet. A protein-rich diet in the early spring is important for ducks during egg production (Birkhead, 1984, 1985).

● Titmus (1979) described the characteristic early summer chironomid emergence peak (late May/early June) which was comprised largely of *Cricotopus sylvestris*, *Cricotopus intersectus*, *Procladius choreus* and *Chironomus* species. *Tanypus* species were more numerous in the

A floating trap used during the research to catch emerging midges

second year of the study. The Great Linford pits were characterised by low midge abundance and a short period (June) of hatching in any significant numbers.

● Street and Titmus (1981) showed that barley straw can provide a suitable substrate for the proliferation of aquatic invertebrates in newly-flooded gravel pit lakes which are poor in organic matter. This practice is probably of limited application except where wildfowl production needs to be maximised on ecologically immature workings.

● Hill (1980) noted that, as in other studies, the mallard at Great Linford timed their nesting so that the peak duckling hatch coincided with peak chironomid emergence. The proportion of both mallard and tufted ducklings fledging from a brood is directly associated with the abundance of hatching chironomids. Whether this is cause and effect is not known with certainty. Mallard broods at Linford spend most time feeding where aquatic invertebrate abundances are highest (Hill, 1983).

● Mallard nest success is highest on islands and where the surrounding vegetation is relatively high. Mallard and tufted duck nests tend to be aggregated in clumps and the proportion of nests lost to predators increases with nest density (ie nest loss is density-dependent) (Hill, 1983).

David Hill radio-tracking mallard broods at Great Linford

● During the early 1980s, most mallard and tufted duck took their broods off the reserve for rearing on the adjacent River Great Ouse, where invertebrate abundance was greater (Hill, 1983, Giles *et al* 1988). This happened despite the fact that mallard duckling mortality increases sharply with home-range size during the early feeding period (Hill, 1983).

Excellent duck nesting habitat created within the reserve

● Duckling mortality was the fey factor explaining 58% of total mallard mortality between years at the WAGBI gravel pit reserve at Sevenoaks, Kent (Hill, 1984). Simulation modelling work indicated that both density-dependent duckling mortality and density-dependent over-winter loss could produce compensatory survival in shot mallard populations, allowing local harvesting rates of around 30% of the autumn population (Hill, 1982, 1983). The ways in which mallard populations are able to compensate for shooting mortality through improved survival rates of the unshot stock need further study. The situation in the wild is complicated by the continental wanderings of wintering birds and the large scale releasing of hand-reared ducks.

Mike Street with a harvest of ducks from the Great Linford site

● Some of the practical findings of the first 12 years of research at Great Linford were published by ARC (Street, 1985) in a booklet 'The Restoration of Gravel Pits for Wildfowl'. This describes the main restoration procedures needed to design and establish a successful winter wildfowl reserve. The key to improving duckling survival came later with the fish-removal research (Giles *et al* 1991). The restoration handbook was expanded and updated in 1989 (Street, 1989)

● The great value of having control of water levels in a wetland waterfowl reserve was established through studies on duckling use of seasonally flooded lake basins. Water level control also benefits migratory wading birds. Where water levels can be drawn down to expose invertebrate-rich sediments during the early spring or late summer, a wide variety of waders will use the site (Street, 1986). Newly inundated shallows tend to be very productive for aquatic invertebrates and so are also good duckling rearing habitat.

Invertebrate-rich mud: full of food for waders and ducklings.

● Hill *et al* (1986) showed that tame mallard ducklings released on to ponds with high fish (bream and roach) densities travelled further in search of food and gained less weight than ducklings feeding over areas of low fish density. The abundance of insects emerging at the pond surface was inversely related to fish density. Fish also reduced the abundance of submerged aquatic plants.

Hand-reared mallard ducklings on an experimental pond

● Cousens (1986, unpublished) showed by computer modelling that if fish were removed, other invertebrate predators would probably move in to exploit any increased food supply. This proved to be true with the colonisation of Main Lake at Great Linford by *Sialis* (Alderfly) larvae after the 1987 fish removal (England, 1991).

● Studies on feral Canada and introduced greylag geese showed that considerable damage was being done to farmland adjacent to the Great Linford reserve (Traill-Stevenson, 1987) and that population control was necessary. Studies on the biology of Great Linford geese showed that island nesting birds were much more successful than mainland nesters, probably because of reduced predation by foxes (Giles & Wright 1987, Wright & Giles, 1988). To curb the population growth by shooting, around 24% of the flock would need to be culled each year - a difficult task (Giles & Street 1990). The picking up of newly-laid eggs (under MAFF licence) appeared to be a humane and potent method of reducing annual gosling production (Giles & Street, 1990) and

A Canada goose defends its nest

has proved to be successful (Wright & Phillips 1991, 1992). Computer modelling confirmed the long-term potential of picking up eggs and substituting them with boiled ones, though the system is labour-intensive (Barnard, 1991).

● Fish studies were developed on several species; notably pike, bream, tench, roach and perch. An intensive study of the population ecology of pike showed that density-dependent cannibalism amongst fry can potentially regulate year classes (Giles *et al*, 1986, Wright & Giles, 1987). Cannibals grow quickly and probably represent the majority of surviving pike in habitats where alternate fish prey are scarce. Where attempts are made on angling waters to increase pike numbers by stocking fry, an upper limit of five fry per square metre is advised.

A pike dissected to reveal a cannibalised younger pike in its stomach

● Prior to 1988, the large weed-free Main Lake supported a high population of large pike (up to 28 pounds) while the weedy St Peters lagoons harboured big numbers of small pike (Wright, 1987). Pike fry survival was good in St Peters but egg and fry mortality was very high (95%) in Main Lake, probably due largely to the silting of eggs (Wright, 1988). In Main Lake, pike ate bream, roach, hybrid breamxroach, perch and other pike. In St Peters the diet was similar, with the addition of tench and bullheads. Overall, roach were the commonest prey. The presence of scarring on many adult pike in Main Lake indicated that attempted (and successful) cannibalism was frequent. Small pike (4-6 pounds) were found to eat mallard ducklings on Main Lake. The removal of large pike probably leads to substantial increases in the survival of small pike via reduced cannibalism, and thus may increase duckling predation rates.

The toothy maw of a large pike. Pike eat pike, other fish and ducklings; the inter-relationships are therefore complicated.

● Studies on tench (Wright & Giles, 1991) and bream (Wright, 1989) showed that these species live for up to around 15 years in gravel pits, with tench preferring weedy hard-bedded lakes like St Peters, while silt-bedded lakes such as Main Lake are more suitable as bream habitat. Main Lake and St Peter's Lake bream were largely produced during the hot summers of the early 1970s, as were the St Peters tench. Cool summers tended to produce weak year classes of both species. Bream dig actively for food on the lake bed, uprooting vegetation and creating turbid water conditions. Tench pick invertebrates from lake bed surface sediments and from plants and thus do not damage weed beds in the way that bream can when they live at high population densities ($>$150kg/ha).

● Surveys of the status of wild brown trout populations (Giles 1989, 1990, 1991) showed that there are considerable conservation problems for the species, involving several forms of habitat degradation and widespread overfishing and stocking with hatchery produced fish. The wild trout research project was developed within The Game Conservancy Trust's wetland research group with a view to researching and ameliorating some of the pressures on wild native trout stocks.

A wild brown trout: the subject of ongoing research by The Game Conservancy.

● Dietary studies on coarse fish at Great Linford (Giles et al 1987, 1988) showed that bream dig deeply on the lake bed for chironomid larvae and small mussels. Perch take chironomid pupae in mid-water, while tench pick chironomid larvae, mayfly nymphs, alderfly larvae, caddis larvae, snails, mussels and a variety of other aquatic invertebrates from plants and lake bottom surfaces. Roach eat either zooplankton (*Daphnia hyalina*) or filamentous green algae. The removal of fish from some of the lakes at Great Linford in October 1987 allowed a rough estimation of fish community densities and consequent rates of food consumption (Giles et al, 1988). This indicated that the abundance of invertebrates (especially chironomids) available to waterfowl (especially ducklings) should increase markedly after fish removal. The growth of aquatic plants was also predicted to increase after fish removal.

Stomach-pumping a bream to obtain dietary information. With due care, the fish can be released unharmed.

● Sampling for aquatic invertebrates and submerged water plants in 1988 and 1989 proved the above predictions to be correct, with large increases in chironomids, snails and other invertebrates both in Main and St Peters lakes. Aquatic plant abundance also increased in St Peters and occurred across the whole bed of the previously weed-free Main Lake (Giles et al, 1989).

● The reintroduction of fish at the original population densities (around 350kg/ha) in sampling bays of both St Peters and Main Lake reversed the fish-removal effects (Giles et al, 1991). Studies of the effects of fish

Weed beds flourish in Main Lake after the removal of the fish in 1987

(bream and perch) on insect abundance in controlled experimental ponds confirmed the field data. It was proved, therefore, that coarse fish populations at normal stock densities significantly depress the abundance of chironomid larvae and snails which are vital foods for downy ducklings (Giles et al, 1991).

A tufted duckling searching the lake bed for food

● Bream growth rates and body condition in gravel pits, and probably in natural lakes, appear to be controlled by competition for the invertebrate food supply. Before the fish removal, when the average chironomid standing crops in Main Lake were around 10g/m^2 bream growth was very slow, with a stunted population stuck at an average weight of around 1.5kg per fish. After the large-scale fish removal, average bream weights increased in one year to 2.2kg and the average chironomid standing crop doubled to around 21g/m^2 (Wright, 1989). Severe competition for aquatic invertebrates is likely to occur in many lake ecosystems.

Bream compete strongly for the midge larvae in lake bed mud

● Laboratory studies on the underwater feeding success of downy ducklings proved that higher densities of chironomid larvae in gravel sediments lead directly to higher numbers of prey items caught per dive (Giles 1989, 1990). This suggested that the improvement in feeding habitat quality produced in the reserve lakes by the fish removal should lead to increased brood use of the lakes and improved duckling survival. There are

strong indications that both these things have happened at Great Linford after the fish removal (Giles, 1990, 1992).

Tufted duck benefit from improved feeding habitats

● Mallard duckling survival also appears to be improving after the fish removal and both shoveler and pochard (a species thought to be in decline in NW Europe) nested successfully in the Great Linford reserve after the fish-removal (Giles et al, 1992). The spectacular increase in weed growth on Main Lake after the fish removal led directly to large increases in the numbers of wintering mute swan, gadwall, coot and pochard (Phillips, 1992).

Shoveler feed by straining small invertebrates through their specialised bills

● Mallard duckling broods at Great Linford are seen most often on lakes with very low fish densities and least often on lakes with either high natural fish stock levels or lakes which have been intensively stocked with fish for angling (Wright & Phillips, 1990). Field feeding experiments with tame mallard ducklings showed that they fared better on areas with low fish densities but tended to lose weight even at these sites. It seems that good duckling survival is critically timed to coincide with peak insect hatches from areas where competition for this vital food source from other animals such as fish is low.

● Pochard wintering at Great Linford were shown to feed over chironomid-rich patches of the lake beds and to eat these larvae during the early winter months (Phillips, 1990). Wintering pochard flocks can detect small differences in chironomid abundance between lakes and

Pochard: on the increase at Great Linford

they may achieve this by searching the environment for food 'hotspots'. Once a profitable feeding area is found, the whole flock can benefit. The sites chosen for feeding were also relatively shallow - this may be important in minimising energy expenditure by the birds (Phillips, 1990).

The fish removed were weighed in order to calculate their impact on the invertebrates.

- The fish removal clearly benefited wildfowl in three ways:-

a) The diversity of nesting duck species increased.
b) Duckling habitat use increased and survival improved.
c) Wintering waterfowl numbers increased substantially in comparison to adjacent control lakes.

Mute swans wintering at Great Linford. Many more were seen after the removal of the fish in 1987.

- Computer simulation modelling techniques are being developed to produce a practical lake management package which will predict the ecological effects of fish removal from gravel pits (Barnard 1989, 1990).

The research team

The following Game Conservancy staff have contributed to the research story which unfolds in the book:

Nigel Gray	(instigator of original idea)
Peter Lees	(first project scientist)
Mike Street	(longest serving scientist and principal reserve planner)
Rosalind Wright	(fish and waterfowl ecologist)
David Hill	(wildfowl population dynamics research student)
Graham Titmus	(aquatic invertebrates research student)
Andrew Traill-Stevenson	(reserve warden and technician)
Christine Tucker	(duckling biology)
Vivien Phillips	(wildfowl biology, reserve management)
Mike Birkhead	(duck breeding ecology)
Stephen Cousens	(computer simulation modelling of lake food web)
Nick Giles	(fish and wildfowl ecology)
Stephen Barnard	(computer simulation modelling fish effects on invertebrate food supply for ducks)

Graham Titmus, David Hill, Rosalind Wright, Sacha Haywood and Steve Barnard all gained doctorates based on their research work at Great Linford.

The science and management have also benefited from the Direction of Dr Dick Potts and Mr Richard Van Oss of The Game Conservancy and Mr Rudolph Agnew, Mr Dennis Hurst, Mr Peter Gawn, Dr Pat Terry, Mr Martin Clarke, Mr John Mortimer and Mr Richard Yerbury of ARC.

Several distinguished scientists have also helped with the design of the research programme, particularly Dr Jeffrey Harrison, Dr Chris Perrins, Dr Myrfyn Owen, Dr Clive Pinder, Professor Ray Beverton, Mr Eddie Shoesmith, Dr Mike Learner, Dr P. Roy Wiles, Professor Alan Brook, Mr Richard Mann, Dr Nicholas Aebischer and Dr Stephen Tapper. To all of these people and to the many others whose help has not been personally acknowledged, we extend our thanks.

CHAPTER 1

GRAVEL PIT RESTORATION: LESSONS LEARNT AT GREAT LINFORD

The first objective of the Great Linford research project was to establish the key aspects of landform which are important for waterfowl habitat. Essentially a system of trial and error was used, with subsequent modification in the light of experience.

The Great Linford Reserve

The map (Figure 1.1) details the wildfowl reserve plan which has been steadily modified and improved for the past 20 years.

The Great Linford sand and gravel pit, worked between the 1940s and the early 80s, is a 300 hectare site in the flood plain of the upper reaches of the River Great Ouse, two kilometres west of Newport Pagnell in Buckinghamshire (Street, 1986). A small proportion of the workings are approximately 50 years old, but the majority are much more recent, having been excavated at a higher rate during the construction phase of Milton Keynes. Most of the wetlands within the study area are therefore ecologically very immature. There are no extensive areas of shallow water (less than 50cm) and much of the area of standing water contains only a low number of submerged aquatic plants. In the remaining water area, the weed beds are restricted by silty sediments, high turbidity, dense fish populations and deep water, so they have not yet developed. All the lake beds are composed of a mixture of gravel, sand and clay on an underlying stratum of Oxford clay. Many areas have thick sub-aquatic accumulations of mineral silt, and only in the older parts of the quarry are there any significant amounts of the organically rich sediments associated with high biological productivity.

The area managed by The Game Conservancy as a wildfowl reserve occupies approximately 37 hectares of the site, more or less centrally placed. It consists of 17 hectares of open water (Main Lake) from 0.5 to 4.5m deep with an average depth of 1.5m, plus a 10.5 hectare complex of islands and lagoons in the south

west corner (St Peters Lake) 0.5 - 2.5m deep. The ratio of land to water in this island/lagoon complex is 3.1:1 and there is 0.74km of shoreline per hectare. This small area was left in this condition following

Figure 1.1 The main features of the Great Linford wildfowl reserve in the 1980s; some modifications have been made subsequently. Main Lake is used principally as a winter refuge and brood-rearing area whilst St Peters and Stanton Low are important nesting areas.

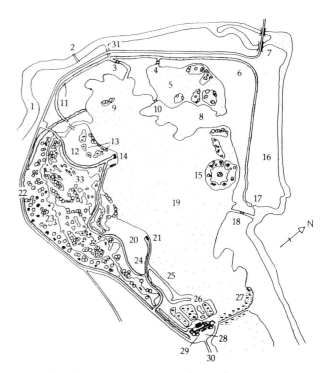

1. R. Great Ouse	17. Canal overspill weir
2. Pipe Bridge	18. Main Lake outlet sluice
3. Inlet sluice	19. Main Lake
4. Inlet sluice	20. Marsh area
5. Stanton Low Lake	21. Near Hide
6. Wet meadow	22. Hedge to screen breeding sanctuary
7. Mill Weir	23. Ossier coppice
8. Goose lawn and loafing spit	24. Screened path to the hide
9. Tern island	25. Shingle loafing spit
10. Outlet sluice	26. The Front Ponds
11. Security canal	27. Reed bed
12. Nestling meadow	28. Car park
13. Wader scrapes	29. ARC Wildfowl Centre
14. Far Hide	30. Approach road
15. The Hollow Island	31. Connection to river
16. Grazing pasture	32. Experimental ponds
	33. St Peters Lake

Aerial photograph of the Great Linford wildfowl reserve

The gravel digging barge outside the original wildfowl laboratory at Great Linford.

The silt on the floor of the shallow, wet dug Main Lake is easily disturbed in a storm.

Lakes with a silt-laden floor can still generate submerged aquatic plants, but it may be necessary to reduce the fish population.

piecemeal excavation and tipping. The remaining 8.5 hectare is permanent unimproved pasture around Main Lake. The Great Linford site was selected partly because of its central geographical location and the fact that it was already used by relatively large numbers of wintering wildfowl. Chiefly, however, this particular lake and its surroundings were seen to have the best potential for development as a duck breeding sanctuary and winter refuge.

Methods of excavation

Gravel pits can be excavated in two main ways - wet or dry dug (Giles, 1987). Both types of pit were present at the Linford site and they were created in the following ways:-

1. Wet digging (Reserve Main Lake)

When the workings are opened up, groundwater is present at water table level and extraction proceeds from underwater, the gravel being sucked from the bed of the newly forming lake with a suction dredger and deposited in a floating barge. The dense aggregate rapidly settles out in the barge and silt-laden water flows directly back into the lake to form a thick carpet of loose sediment on the new lake bed. The aggregate is then taken by barge to the grading plant. Wet-dug pits today are normally excavated using a drag line.

2. Dry digging (St Peters Lake)

The topsoil and subsoil (overburden) above the deposit is stripped off and is either stored or taken away. The groundwater entering the quarry is continuously pumped out during excavation. The dry excavated sand and gravel is transported from the pit by conveyor belt or dumper truck to a washing and grading plant. The washings (tailings) from the plant are run off into silt settlement lagoons. Once the settled silt reaches the water surface, it begins to dry out and consolidate, allowing colonisation by plants. Silt lagoons often develop into excellent conservation habitats. Once the deposit is worked out, overburden and topsoil may be bulldozed back into the dry quarry to landscape the banks. When pumping ceases the pit normally fills up with water (subject to the water table level).

13

The outcome of these two differing operations has been to create two lake types on the Great Linford complex described in the Table 1.1 below.

The wet dug lakes typically have a poorly developed aquatic plant community and a rather species-poor invertebrate population. The drifting sediments are colonised by large numbers of midge larvae, worms and mussels and the open water by zooplankton and water boatmen. Wet dug pits can be stimulated into plant production by fish-removal.

The dry dug lakes are clear, with good light penetration. They have many dense weedbeds with a variety of plant species and a diverse invertebrate community. Dry dug pits are in general more attractive to breeding and overwintering waterfowl.

Aquatic plants normally spread and become dominant in older lakes but at Great Linford, the older (wet dug) lakes lack submerged vegetation. The disturbance of sediment which reduces light penetration is caused both by wind turbulence and by lake bed feeding bream, carp, tench and roach. As the silt settles again, it suppresses the growth of aquatic plant seedlings.

The weed beds of the dry dug lakes include water lilies, crowfoots, milfoil, hornwort, pondweeds, starwort, stonewort, duck weed, irises, rushes, sedges, grasses and reeds. These provide habitats for many groups of invertebrates including snails, mussels, shrimps, water lice, leeches, flatworms, midges, water boatmen, beetles, mites, worms and a diverse zooplankton. In contrast only the most sheltered bays of the wet dug pits grew any submerged plants whilst the fish populations were present. Here only Canadian pondweed and fennel-leaved pondweed *Potamogeton pectinatus* formed weed beds.

Dry dug pits have generally greater opportunities for creating suitable habitat. Machines can gain access to create the required range of complex landforms.

The Wildfowl Centre Main Lake is a typical shallow, wet dug gravel pit, with a deep bottom layer of fine flocculant silt which is easily disturbed during windy weather to give turbid, brown water conditions. The dry dug lakes are typically clear watered even during strong winds. To investigate this difference, ten 0.5 litre water samples were collected each day from two exposed wet dug lakes (Main Lake and Black Horse Lake) and two similarly exposed dry dug lakes (Haversham, Bradwell) during spring gales in March 1986. The water samples were taken from just below the surface on each occasion and then filtered on pre-weighed glass fibre filter papers (retaining particles of 1.2 micrometres and larger) and oven dried to constant weight. The dry film remaining on the paper contained both organic (eg plankton) and inorganic (eg clay) material. To separate these fractions the organic material was burnt off at 450°C for several hours in a muffle furnace. The inorganic content could then be assessed by subtraction of the original filter paper weight.

At the height of a storm (March 24 1986) the mean inorganic silt loadings of the four lakes were:

WET DUG   DRY DUG
Main   177 mg/l   Haversham 1.6 mg/l
Black Horse   194 mg/l   Bradwell   7.7 mg/l

The dry dug lakes carried virtually no clay sediments and remained clear, whilst the wet dug lakes were mixed to a uniform chocolate brown colour.

Table 1.1. Major characteristics of some of the Linford Lakes.

Extraction method	Lake	Age (Years)	Development of plant communities	Diversity of invertebrate communities
(a) wet dug	Main Lake	20+	poor	low
	Black Horse	20+	poor	low
	Rocla	30+	poor	low
	Red House	30+	poor	low
(b) dry-dug	St. Peter's	20	very good	high
	Dovecote	18	good	high
	Trout	20	very good	high
	Haversham	11	developing well	developing
	Bradwell	9	developing well	developing

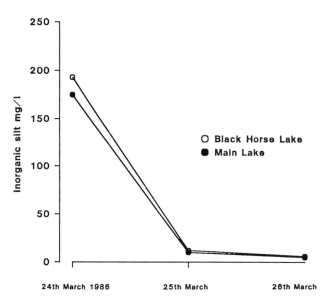

Figure 1.2 The sedimentation rate of inorganic silt on Main Lake and Black Horse Lake, after the spring 1986 gales. Most of the silt stirred up by the storm settles out after only 24 hours, coating any underwater plants with a layer of clay particles.

Figure 1.2 shows the sedimentation rate after the gale (March 25 and 26) of the two wet dug gravel pits. Clearly both behave in a very similar way, with over 90% of the silt settling out in the first 24 hours after the storm. As Main and Black Horse lakes are both about 20 years old (they were originally a single lake) it seems that left unmanaged they would take a long period to develop diverse plant communities. Indeed, had we not intervened, the high population density of fish (especially bream) might have maintained the weed-free state indefinitely.

The 1987 fish removal from the previously weed-free Main Lake (see Chapter 7) illustrated that the bream and roach had been having a fundamentally important effect upon submerged weed growth. In 1988 the whole lake bed was covered in a luxuriant growth of aquatic vegetation. Black Horse Lake, which had no fish removed, has remained virtually weed-free to this day and is a successful coarse fishery. Fish have a potent effect on the ecology of the lakes in which they live.

Encouraging aquatic plants

Management to remove fish allows plant seedlings to germinate from the seed bank in the lake bed sediments and to grow in relatively clear water. Once the roots of aquatic plants have stabilised the soft mud, it becomes more difficult for wind action to stir it up and so, progressively, the lake develops a stable submerged aquatic flora. These plants then provide food for a wide variety of waterfowl and a home for a diverse and abundant invertebrate community.

Landform: Key points for reserve design

In the early 1970s Main Lake and St Peters were modified with earth-moving machinery to provide specific habitat features for waterfowl.

Mike Street's handbook 'The Restoration of Gravel Pits for Wildfowl', published by ARC in 1985 details the physical landforms produced within the Great Linford reserve to benefit waterfowl and other wetland wildlife. The key topographical features which have proved their value over the past 20 years are as follows:

Security of the wildfowl reserve

The erection of a fence excluded grazing animals and allowed ground cover to grow up, dominated by tufted hair grass (*Deschampsia caespitosa*). This had the immediate effect of making the reserve more attractive to ground nesting waterfowl.

Disturbance within the breeding sanctuary part of the reserve (St Peters Lake, the island/lagoon complex in the south-west corner) was further reduced by the restriction of anglers to certain zones of the lake shore well away from this area. When fishing ceased completely in 1979 there was a marked increase in the number of birds making regular use of the reserve.

A security canal (Figures 1.1 and 1.3) was dug around the breeding sanctuary to isolate the islands from the mainland and to restrict ground predators (two-legged as well as four!). The canal forms an effective barrier. A wide belt of reeds and rushes was grown on the inner side.

Figure 1.3 A security canal like this makes the ideal reserve boundary, it reduces disturbance and provides good habitat.

The second 'line of defence' at Great Linford, after the security canal, is a thorn hedge which was planted between 1972 and 1975. The area immediately inside the hedge was planted with sallows and willows (*Salix sps.*) which are established and coppiced in a three year rotation in linear strips parallel to the perimeter hedge. These further thicken the screen and provide a range of valuable habitats for small birds, mammals and insects, as well as good quality nesting cover for waterfowl. The inner edge of this osier coppice follows the line of the security canal.

Minimising disturbance

Landform is the basis of subsequent habitat development. The overall design should aim to minimise the disturbance by visitors to birds and other wildlife. Screened banks and sunken walkways, combined with well positioned hides and observation towers will allow good viewing of birds with little intrusion. In a restored complex with a series of lakes, a wildlife reserve should be sited at the sheltered, relatively inaccessible end, upwind of the lake complex and well away from recreational activities such as water skiing, jet skiing and power boating. Coarse fisheries which are heavily stocked with carp or bream are not suitable as waterfowl reserve lakes and it is unlikely that on small gravel pits (less than 2ha) any fishing activity is compatible with high quality waterfowl habitat.

Control of water level

Control of water depth is of paramount value to the wetland manager as it allows the wetting of scrapes and shallows and maintains water barriers (against foxes) to near-shore islands. Drawing down (lowering) lakes greatly facilitates fish removal and, if prolonged, will promote a breakdown of the sediments and plant nutrient release. If the draw down is extended over a year, terrestrial seedlings will germinate and grow before being killed after re-flooding. This plant material will then rapidly rot, providing valuable food for detritus-feeding aquatic invertebrates which are potential waterfowl food.

Wet meadows

At Great Linford marginal meadows can be deliberately flooded from early winter through to the following spring (mid March) by using sluice systems. The wet grassland washes provide very useful feeding grounds for snipe, curlew, redshank, greenshank, godwits and ruffe. Wet meadows are now a rare habitat in the UK.

Reed beds and sheltered shallow bays

Water level control also allows the long-term maintenance of shallow lagoons where common reed (*Phragmites*) flourishes. It is extremely desirable in conservation terms to create large (> 2ha) reed beds as they will attract and harbour species such as bearded tits, bitterns and marsh harriers, together with the commoner reed and sedge warblers and reed buntings. Reeds also provide autumn roosts for swallows, yellow wagtails, house martins, reed and corn buntings. Reed beds can be burnt on a rotational basis to clear out the dry dead stems which tend progressively to raise the level of the bed above water and allow tree seedlings to take root. Shallow reeded lagoons seldom

The basic landforms for a wildlife reserve should be created before the heavy extraction machinery leaves the site.

have water over 1.5m depth (the least valuable zone for most aquatic wildlife). Sheltered wide shallows of around 0.5m, grading back to zero at the shore, will develop a rich organic mud abundant in weed growth and with a high diversity of aquatic invertebrates; ideal feeding areas for ducklings of all species as well as adult teal, shoveler, mallard, gadwall, swans, dabchick, herons and kingfishers. The deeper water beyond will be exploited by pochard, tufted ducks, wintering goldeneye and even smew during a cold snap of weather.

Deterring predators

A further benefit of deep water is as a deterrent to foxes which will readily wade shallows to reach nesting islands but which appear, at least in our experience, to be less willing to swim longer distances to islands for the chance of a meal of eggs or a sitting duck.

Feeding waders on passage

The control of water depth allows the reserve manager to counteract to a degree the natural seasonal fluctuations in water level (low in summer and autumn, high in winter and spring). Rising water in the spring encourages ducks to nest and the deliberate lowering of lakes to expose invertebrate-rich mud in the spring and late summer is a very successful method of attracting waders on passage (see Chapter 3). Migrating wading birds rapidly drop in to exploit the rich food supply on patches of newly exposed mud, which must appear to them like a muddy marine shoreline revealed by the tide.

Ponds

Water level control on a worked-out gravel pit site allows the long-term maintenance of shallow pools

A purpose-built gravel bank for loafing/moulting waterfowl and nesting plovers.

A mallard sitting on a well concealed nest in rank grassland.

and ponds which are a very valuable habitat for dragonflies, amphibians (frogs, toads, newts), grass-snakes, water voles and many other forms of aquatic life. The deliberate exclusion of fish from such ponds will promote a diverse and abundant invertebrate and amphibian fauna which would otherwise be decimated by fish predation.

Soils

In general the slope on lake shallows should be no greater than 1:15. For flooded grassland it should be in the range of 1:50 - 1:100 (Andrews & Kinsman 1991). All 'good growing' areas (shelterbelt, lake margins, shallows and marshland) should be surfaced with 0.3m of uncompacted topsoil to promote healthy plant growth. Loam soils rich in earthworms are best for good plant growth. The final soil surface should be 0.5 - 0.75 metres above the normal summer water table level. This will provide a moist, high nutrient growing environment for plants.

Subsoil, with its absence of viable weed seeds and low nutrient status, is useful for spreading over other areas as it will not generate strong growths of unwelcome 'weed' species in the way that top-soil does. Subsoil is a suitable basis for rough grassland areas. These should

Benefits of water level control

An ability to adjust the water level in lakes and marshes via a sluice system potentially gives the following benefits:- Raised water levels can be used to flood water meadows in winter, isolate nesting islands in spring/summer from foxes, fill scrapes and pools adjacent to lakes and re-fill drawn down lakes, killing terrestrial vegetation.

Lowering water levels is a very good method of drawing in migrating shorebirds to wet mud feeding sites, improving light penetration to establish submerged weed growth, netting out abundant fish populations and periodically drying out large areas of lake bed to promote aquatic productivity.

The initial costs of installing a reserve water level control system (including pumps where necessary) are usually well justified in the long-term by the wide range of benefits accruing from the investment.

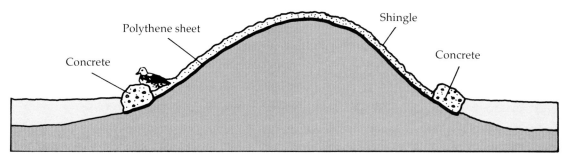

Figure 1.4 Shingle covered beaches underlain with thick black polythene make attractive, low-profile, weed-free and low maintenance loafing areas.

not be fertilised and annual grazing or hay-making keeps soil fertility low and promotes botanical and invertebrate species diversity.

Recently disturbed soils tend to be quickly colonised by docks and thistles. Use of a herb/grass mix of suitable local native species appropriate to the soil conditions is preferable to allowing ground to vegetate naturally. During establishment, sown areas should be cut every 6 to 8 weeks to establish cover. This will prevent erosion and the invasion of troublesome species. On poor soils the use of a nurse crop of a quick germinating but short-lived grass such as Westerwolds rye can be helpful.

Resting areas

The need for a safe day roost is especially important in the winter months for large flocks of immigrant birds. However, birds roosting on a lake - especially in windy conditions - must expend valuable energy in order to 'keep station' on the water and in rough weather they much prefer to rest on land. To help the reserve attract and hold a high density of roosting waterfowl, several safe, sheltered, shore-based roosting or 'loafing' sites were provided where the birds can see the approach of potential predators and have unimpeded access to open water. Sheep graze the vegetation of an elevated bank on the north-west shore of Main Lake and this has become a popular loafing spot for ducks.

In 1978, a 'purpose-built' loafing bank was made in the Great Linford reserve (Figure 1.4). This was surfaced with black polythene sheet, anchored by a 0.2m layer of 6 to 18mm gravel spread evenly over it, the combined effect being to suppress the growth of plants. Ducklings also benefit from areas devoid of dense vegetation. They should not have to struggle through dense wet vegetation to reach these resting sites.

Rough grassland

This can be seeded with a sparse sowing of native grass species and managed on a 3-year cycle to halt scrub invasion. Rough grassland 0.25m-1m tall provides habitat for many species of grasshopper, butterfly, amphibian, reptile, small mammals and hunting raptors (eg barn owl). These benefits are in addition to nesting ducks (mallard, shoveler, gadwall) redshanks and lapwings. The losses of duck nests to egg predators like crows and magpies is greatly reduced where the habitat is comprised of dense, tall overwintered grass tussocks. Where these occur along the base of hedgerows, grey partridge may nest.

Existing grasslands can, on rare occasions, be relocated during restoration by moving thick (0.3-0.5m) turves. This has the benefit of retaining the wildflower seed bank in the transferred top-soil. Much of the natural invertebrate fauna will also survive the move. Turves must be carefully handled and transplanted on to non-compacted weed-free subsoil with a summer water table within approx 0.7m of the final soil surface. Note that wildflower-rich rough grassland is a low-nutrient system which can be sustained by annual haymaking - no fertilisers should be applied to the system and any cut vegetation should be removed.

Leaving a gravel pit to colonise and develop naturally results in the establishment of a plant community dominated by one or two stongly competitive species, usually willow and alder, with a low floral diversity, and Milne (1974) showed that a decline in bird species at an unmanaged gravel pit after a few years was due to the increasing uniformity of the vegetation as naturally colonising vigorous species of plant became dominant. Continuous management is therefore vital if the restoration is aimed at a truly diverse nature reserve.

Wet woodland

Wet woodland habitat is becoming a UK rarity and is well worth preserving and establishing wherever possible. Dead standing timber should be left to rot *in situ* as it affords a home for many wood-boring beetles and thus a food source for greater and lesser-spotted woodpeckers, treecreepers and nuthatches.

Wet woodland: a declining habitat well worth preserving and creating.

Old trees also provide nest sites for tawny owls, tits, treecreepers, stock doves and woodcock (on drier patches at ground level). Willows, oak and birch are especially species-rich and should be encouraged in favour of non-native species. Even-aged woods which were planted with only one or two tree species are much poorer biologically than a woodland with 6 to 8 tree species and a similar number of native shrubs. Saplings should be deer and rabbit-protected with stiff plastic grow-tubes.

Ecological succession of the botanical community

It is critical to realise that wetlands are always changing; open water succeeding naturally to reedbed, and then drying out to become willow carr and eventually woodland. This process of ecological succession can be halted at given stages by active habitat management in differing reserve areas to produce a complex mosaic of open

water, submerged weed beds, reedbeds, willow/alder scrub and wet woodland. Riverside meadows can be managed to allow winter flooding, providing washes which attract large flocks of wintering waterfowl.

The choice of aquatic vegetation

Marginal aquatic plants grow best in soils up to 0.15m above the water table, whilst emergent species grow in water up to around 1m depth. Submerged species like water depths down to perhaps 10m, and deeper in lakes where the water is very clear (Figure 1.5). Stoneworts are able to grow at considerable depths in clear marl lakes such as some of those in the disused quarry sites of the Cotswold Water Park. However, in many lakes poor light penetration prevents growth below about 3m depth. From this it is clear that many of the (unrestored) early post-war deep, steep-sided flooded gravel pits provide very poor habitats for the development of a diverse aquatic flora.

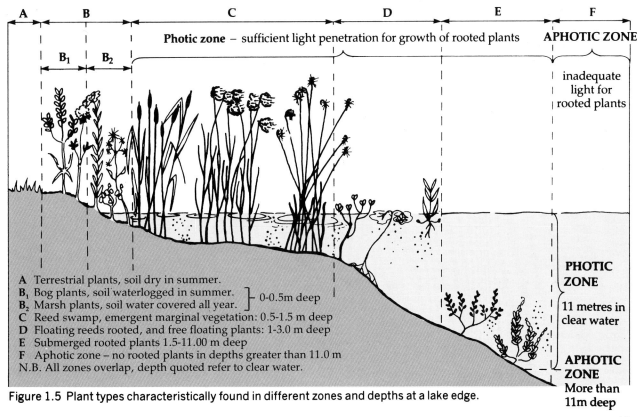

A Terrestrial plants, soil dry in summer.
B₁ Bog plants, soil waterlogged in summer. ⎤ 0-0.5m deep
B₂ Marsh plants, soil water covered all year. ⎦
C Reed swamp, emergent marginal vegetation: 0.5-1.5 m deep
D Floating reeds rooted, and free floating plants: 1-3.0 m deep
E Submerged rooted plants 1.5-11.00 m deep
F Aphotic zone – no rooted plants in depths greater than 11.0 m
N.B. All zones overlap, depth quoted refer to clear water.

Figure 1.5 Plant types characteristically found in different zones and depths at a lake edge.

Table 1.2 provides a list of aquatic plant species suitable for planting on gravel pit sites and found in the zones described in Figure 1.5.

Plant-rich shallows provide seeds for late summer/autumn duck food and harbour aquatic invertebrates vital for the early nutrition of ducklings. Both ducklings and adult ducks feed avidly in productive shallow scrapes and lagoons. Table 1.3 provides information on the plants favoured by waterfowl.

Table 1.2 Plant species suitable for gravel pits. Typically found in zones as in Figure 1.5.

Zone:	A	B1	B2	C	D	E
Alders	X	X				
Great willowherb	X	X				
Forget-me-not	X	X				
Woundwort	O	X				
Gipsy-wort	O	X	O			
Marsh marigold	O	X	O			
Sweet flag		O	X	O		
Flowering rush		O	X	O		
Spike rush		O	X	O		
Water plantain		O	X	X		
Jointed rush		X	X			
Willows	X	X	O			
Bur-marigold	X	X	O			
Sea club-rush		O	X	X		
Reedmace		O	X	X		
Brooklime		X	X	O		
Water cress		X	X	O		
Water mint		X	X	O		
Great water dock		X	X	X		
Marestail		X	X	X		
Meadowsweet	X	X	O			
Hard rush	O	X	X			
Soft rush	O	X	X			
Reed canary grass	O	X	X	O		
Bog bean	O	X	X	O		
Marsh horsetail	O	X	X	O		
Pond sedges	O	X	X	O		
Purple loosestrife	O	X	X	O		
Yellow iris	O	X	X	O		
Great yellow cress	O	X	X	O		
Bur-reed	O	X	X	X		
Reed grass	O	X	X	X		
Common reed	O	X	X	X		
Bulrush			O	X		
Arrowhead		X	O	O		
Duckweed			X	X	X	
Amphibious bistort	X	X	X	X	X	X
Water lilies			O	X	X	
Quillwort			O	X	X	
Water crowfoot			O	O	X	X
Water lobelia			O	X	X	X
Broad-leaved pondweed			O	O	X	X
Water parsnip			O	O	X	X
Lesser water parsnip			O	O	X	X
Bladderwort			O	O	X	X
Water soldier			O	O	X	X
Frogbit			O	O	X	X
Hornwort			O	O	X	O
Canadian pondweed			O	O	X	X
Spiked milfoil			O	O	X	X
Whorled milfoil			O	O	X	X
Stonewort				O	O	X

Key X Species characteristically found in this zone
O Species sometimes found in this zone

Table 1.3 The value of some plants to wildfowl
The following aquatic plants are particularly valuable for waterfowl and should be deliberately established in suitable wetland reserves.

Species	Growth Habit	Value	Uses
Watercrowfoots	Submerged	E	IS(V)
Tassel pondweed (Wigeon grass)	Submerged	U	VSI
Canadian pondweed	Submerged	G	SI
Milfoil	Submerged	E	I(V)
Horned pondweed	Submerged	E	I(V)
Fennel-leaved pondwood (Sago pondwood)	Submerged	VG	IS
Hornwort			I
Starwort	Submerged	U	I(V)
Duckweeds	Submerged and floating leaved	VG	V
Broad-leaved pondweed	Free-floating	VG	I
	Floating leaved	G	I(V)
*Amphibious bistort	Floating leaved	VG	V
*Water lilies	Floating leaved	G	SI
Arrowhead	Emergent in shallows	E	ISB
*Marestail	Emergent in shallows	VG	IB
*Bur-reed	Emergent in shallows and on wet soils	VG	IVB ISB
Spike rush	Emergent in shallows	VG	IS(N)
Sea club-rush	Emergent in shallows	E	
Sedges	Emergent in shallows and on wet soils	VG	SIB
Yellow Iris	Emergent in shallows and on wet soils	U	SIB(N) ISN
*Common (Norfolk) reed	Emergent in moderate depth, to damp soils	G	I(N)
Bulrush	Emergent from moderate depth	U	W(N)(1)
*Reedmace	Emergent from moderate depth to wet soils	G	IS(N)
Rushes	Wet to damp soils	E	IW(N)

Brambles, Nettles
Thistles, Willowherb,
Purple loosestrife,
Tufted hair-grass (N)

* These species can cause problems by choking very shallow water, reducing its value to wildfowl.

Key

Value
E - Excellent   G- Good
VG - Very Good   U - Useful

Uses
I - Harbours invertebrates as food
B - Attractive to broods
S - Seeds readily eaten
N - Used for nesting
V - Vegetation eaten
W - Provides winter cover
( ) -Limited use

A new island constructed during the restoration programme.

Constructing peninsulas on Main Lake at Great Linford.

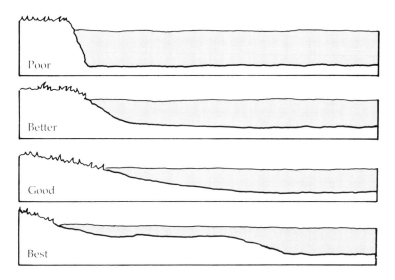

Figure 1.6 The best bank profiles produce a wide shallow (littoral) zone for the development of large areas of submerged weed bed and invertebrate-rich duckling feeding areas.

Islands and shallows

The benefits of wide shallow shorelines of gradual slope, with their diverse floral community, cannot be over-stated. Early post-war gravel pits were usually left as steep-sided flooded holes in the ground which developed an impoverished aquatic flora and fauna attracting mostly wintering diving ducks (eg tufted duck - a species which can exploit the deep water habitat). Carefully restored modern gravel pits should have bank profiles like the best shown in Figure 1.6.

Productive shallows can be established in two further ways:-

a) Via an undulating lake bed deliberately restored to have shallow shoals and deeper channels (Figure 1.7)

b) By the construction of islands and peninsulas.

Ideally islands should combine a complex shoreline with downwind bays for shelter. They should be surrounded by carefully placed top-soil (0.15-0.2m deep)

which will support luxuriant growths of invertebrate-rich aquatic vegetation. All lake shallows should be restored with a covering of top-soil (carefully stored after stripping off prior to extraction) to promote the subsequent growth of aquatic plants. During periods of strong winds wildfowl will choose to shelter behind well designed islands like those in Figure 1.8.

Islands within our own St Peters Lake complex are routinely managed in winter by cutting willow, alder and other shading vegetation to encourage the development of the thick herbaceous ground cover favoured by nesting waterfowl. Useful species are tall tussock-forming grasses eg tufted hairgrass (*Deschampsia caespitosa*), hard and soft rushes (*Juncus*), nettles (*Urtica dioica*), willowherb (*Epilobium sp*), cow parsley (*Ahthriscus sp*), hogweeds (*Heracleum*), bushy coppiced willows, gorse (*Ulex sp*), and bramble. Dead vegetation still standing, or dead hedges of cut branches left after winter, provide vital cover for mallard nesting in the early spring (late February or March). The requirements of feeding habitat for ducks are detailed in Chapter 2.

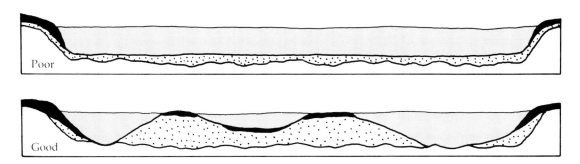

Figure 1.7 Instead of using the overburden and top-soil to make a uniform level lake bed it must be used to create variety and structure in the final lake.

22

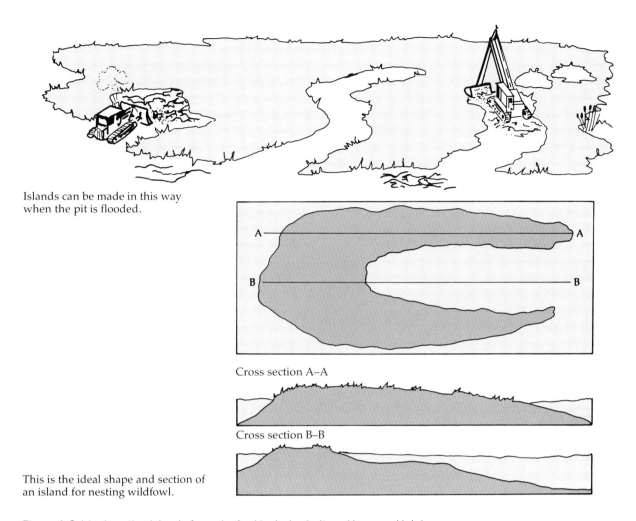

Islands can be made in this way
when the pit is flooded.

Cross section A–A

Cross section B–B

This is the ideal shape and section of
an island for nesting wildfowl.

Figure 1.8 Ideal nesting islands for waterfowl include sheltered bays and inlets.

Islands.

The construction of many offshore low profile
islands, especially with large, sheltered bays in the
lee of prevailing winds, provides many conservation
benefits. The islands provide fox-proof nesting
sites and if covered by rough grassland, nettles and
bramble, provide good duck nesting cover, safe
from predators such as crows and magpies.
Shallows around the islands promote the growth of
submerged weed beds, with their rich invertebrate
communities providing vital insect food resources
for ducklings of all species. Shallow water diving
ducks such as pochard can feed in the marginal
zones around islands, returning to loafing areas at
the head of sheltered bays. Such loafing areas are
used by all waterfowl throughout the winter and
during the annual summer moult when they are
flightless and vulnerable to predators.

A Canada goose nest on an artifical raft. Such features can be useful supplements to restored habitats.

Shelterbelts

Shelterbelts (Figure 1.9) are best planted at right angles to the prevailing winds. Planting should create permeable structures which absorb wind energy rather than solid stands of timber which simply deflect the wind over the tree tops, giving little shelter further downwind. Strong winds allowed to act across a long fetch of water will create wave action against downwind shores which can destroy shallow water plant communities and cause highly turbid conditions. At best, a shelterbelt will decrease

Wildfowl will choose to roost in the lee of islands made like this.

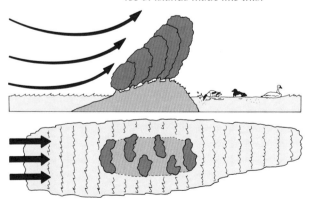

Figure 1.9 Shelterbelts should be designed to absorb and dissipate wind energy, rather than simply deflecting it upward and over a solid barrier.

wind energy no further than 30 times its height downwind (Andrews & Kinsman 1991). A 5m high moderately permeable shelterbelt of trees will thus create a relatively tranquil stretch of water for up to 150 metres downwind. Wind fetch effects can be decreased by building submerged banks which break the waves at intervals down a lake.

Protection from erosion

Wave washed shores can be protected from severe erosion damage by using cobbles, willow staking (which grows into a living screen), floating log (telegraph pole) booms, elm boarding, dead alder pole staking, or the construction of an inshore submerged wave break. This can be stabilised by the use of coarse gravel and cobbles which are stable under storm conditions.

Moulting sites

Ideally, islands should include a sheltered, very shallow sloping bay where a bare sand and gravel shoreline extends for 5 to 10m from the waters edge. If this is underlaid with thick plastic sheeting during construction, it will serve both as a favoured nesting site for terns, little-ringed plover and ringed plover and as a safe moulting site for ducks, geese and swans. Wildfowl lose all of their primary feathers in a single summer moult and, at this time, are flightless and particularly vulnerable to mammalian predators (fox and mink). Safe moult sites on islands are therefore of great value to post-breeding waterfowl populations.

Artificial sand martin and kingfisher nest sites

Sheer faces of aggregate (sand or fine gravel) are favoured nesting habitats for sand martins and kingfishers. Sand martin colonies can sometimes be established by the provision of 1m lengths of 0.1m diameter sand-filled plastic pipe, dug in at 0.2m spacings across the face of a well consolidated aggregate face. Such nest sites are essentially predator-proof and can be very successful in the conservation of these attractive birds. A cement cap across the bottom half of the pipe entrance serves as a stimulus for the birds to enter the pipe and begin nest site excavation. Kingfishers will sometimes adopt sheer vertical soil faces for nest sites if there is a high proportion of sand and gravel to allow easy digging and if the site is relatively close to water.

Around the edges of restored lakes, shallow scrapes can be filled with well-rotted farmyard manure. This will prove very attractive as feeding habitat to wintering snipe and will promote a rich growth of algae and thriving invertebrate populations in adjacent lake shallows fertilised by run-off from the scrapes. Wading birds on passage north in the spring, or south in the late summer, will flock into such areas to feed in the rich shallow water, picking invertebrates from the lake bed surface or probing the mud for burrowing prey like worms and midge larvae. Care should be taken not to over-enrich freshwater systems as this can lead directly to algal blooms, a loss of submerged weed species, low dissolved oxygen concentrations and foul smelling water.

To promote the initial development of an organically-rich lake bed, barley straw can be added to shallow areas of newly-flooded gravel pit lakes. The straw provides a substrate for the growth of fungi and bacteria which provide food for a variety of aquatic invertebrates. These in turn provide food for the birds.

An ideal wader scrape within the Great Linford Reserve. The art is to cater for as many habitat requirements as possible.

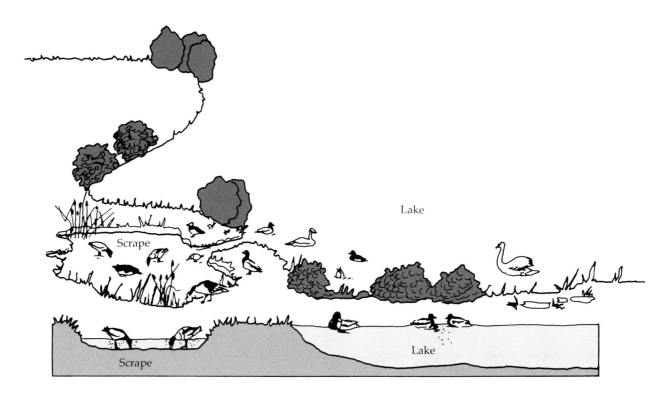

Figure 1.10 Additional feeding sites and scrapes can be made along the lake margins · if the water is allowed to 'follow the machine' it is easy to work to the necessary depth.

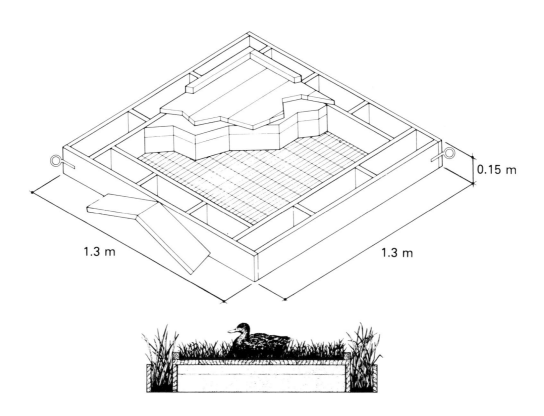

1.3 m

1.3 m

0.15 m

Figure 1.11 This box section nesting raft is ideal for a single nest. The cavity is filled with polystyrene and the rings are to allow the raft to be anchored.

Retrospective gravel pit reserve development

Ideally, all conservation schemes based on worked-out mineral sites should be planned from the outset and incorporated into an initial planning application for permission to extract minerals. However, there are a large number of old, maturing gravel pits in southern English river flood plain sites which were dug 40 to 50 years ago and have been left un-restored as steep-sided, often relatively deep, biologically un-productive waters. What can be done to encourage wildlife conservation in such places?

Margins can be re-graded and inert infill can be imported to create shallow lake edges, peninsulas, islands, bunds and convoluted shorelines, thus maximising the valuable land/water interface habitats. Where the water is too deep to create natural islands, floating nest rafts (Figure 1.11) can be constructed to encourage nesting by ducks, terns, grebes and, in northern areas, divers. Ducks need a soil-covered raft

with a rank grassland herbage, whilst terns prefer a clean gravel surface (underlaid with a thick plastic sheet). Plant growth underwater can be encouraged by felling shading trees and by netting out adult coarse fish, especially bream and carp which feed on the lake bed and constantly uproot germinating aquatic plant seedlings. Fish removal from old established gravel pits has many waterfowl conservation benefits including the following:

1. Reducing the predation of ducklings by small pike. Large pike are less of a problem (Chapter 6).

2. Increasing the invertebrate food supply for ducklings.

3. Increasing aquatic plant growth as invertebrate habitat and food for pochard, swans, coots and gadwall.

Table 1.4 summarises some of the habitat requirements of water birds which might be encouraged to live on restored gravel pit nature reserves (see page 28).

Concluding comments

The most cost-effective and successful gravel pit conservation schemes are those based upon progressive working and restoration. They are planned by landscape architects and ecologists from the outset and implemented by the committed employees of mineral operators who are keen to see positive results. It is a pleasure to record that ARC have used the research findings of The Game Conservancy's Great Linford research not only to restore many of their own sites to high quality nature reserves but also to provide information for other private and public organisations to do likewise. This altruistic attitude has deservedly earned ARC a good reputation in the field of mineral restoration practice. Their 20 year funding of The Game Conservancy's Great Linford research unit is seen as a milestone in industrial sponsorship of applied ecological research.

Improving unrestored flooded gravel pits

Deep, steep-sided pits can be restored retrospectively by using inert infill (sub-soil) to create shallows, peninsulas, bunds and islands. Income can be generated from infilling whilst the habitat is improved. In very deep areas, nesting rafts provide relatively safe sites for breeding ducks, terns, grebes and even divers in northern locations. Weed bed growth can be stimulated by felling dense stands of bankside trees and through the removal of fish such as bream and carp. Large relatively deep gravel pits sometimes harbour large flocks of wintering tufted ducks and pochard which are able to feed on the benthic invertebrates (mussels, snails, insect larvae) living in the mud. In summer, breeding ducks will use scrub and bankside rough grassland where island nest sites are limited. Island space is often monopolised by Canada geese which may require population management to curb their destruction of duck nesting cover.

Table 1.4: Key habitat requirements for waterfowl on gravel pits.

Habitat and predation

	Safe winter roosts and moulting areas	Nesting islands with no trees and dense cover	Marginal reed bed habitat	Bank grassland for nesting	Spring/summer control of corvid and/or fox predation and mink
Mallard	X	X		X	X
Gadwall	X		X	X	X
Teal	X			X	X
Shoveler	X			X	X
Pochard	X		X		X
Tufted duck	X	X			X
Ruddy duck	X	X			X
Greylag goose	X	X		X	X
Canada goose	X		X	X	X
Mute swan	X		X		
Coot	X		X		
Moorhen	X		X		
Great crested grebe					
Dabchick	X				
Heron	X				
Water rail			X		
Bittern			X		

Food

	Abundant small fish and amphibians	Invertebrate-rich brood-rearing habitat	Shallows rich in plant seeds & invertebrates	Deeper water with abundant invertebrates	Abundant submerged water plants
Mallard		X			
Gadwall		X			X
Teal		X	X		
Shoveler		X	X		
Pochard		X		X	X
Tufted duck		X		X	
Ruddy duck		X		X	
Greylag goose					
Canada goose					
Mute swan					X
Coot					X
Moorhen			X		
Great crested grebe	X	X			
Dabchick		X	X		
Heron	X				
Water rail					
Bittern	X				

CHAPTER 2

MALLARD AND TUFTED DUCK BREEDING ECOLOGY

Duck population dynamics

At the start of the Great Linford project The Game Conservancy asked the question:

How can we manage gravel pit duck populations so that they produce enough birds to repopulate adjacent wetlands (where production may be low), to make up for the loss of our natural wetlands, and incidently allow sustainable levels of wildfowling?

David Hill researched some basic aspects of duck population ecology in order to identify the principal phases of mortality operating during the mallard life cycle. He also used a computer to model the likely responses of duck populations to hunting. Duckling mortality was the key factor (main source of variation in annual mallard mortality) in an analysis of data from the Sevenoaks gravel pit reserve in Kent (Hill, 1984), explaining 58% of total mortality between years.

The Sevenoaks reserve, set up by Dr Jeffrey Harrison, has a longstanding association with BASC, (formerly WAGBI) and is one of the few gravel pit sites where ecological information has been recorded over a long period of time. This feature made Hill's study possible. The success of increasing duckling survival at Great Linford in recent years (see later sections in this chapter) shows that gravel pit duck populations can be highly productive with correct management. The increased numbers of ducks surviving at the end of the autumn are then available either for wildfowlers or to populate other areas, boosting home-bred UK duck stocks. Gravel pits are potentially of high conservation value for duck breeding and can, therefore, be established as genuine production areas contrary to the old fashioned view of them being sterile unproductive ecosystems.

If the feeding and nesting conditions are managed correctly then ducks will breed successfully on gravel pit reserves. Moreover, through successful breeding,

populations can produce a crop of birds which can sustain a degree of exploitation through shooting. Wildfowling is a popular pastime and inland shooting areas which offer a combination of duck and goose shooting together with rough shooting or driven pheasants can derive a considerable income from a sporting lease. Critical to the successful management of a hunted species is an understanding of when the key phases of mortality occur during the life cycle; what causes mortality; and whether mortalities are additive or compensatory. Shooting can either impose additive mortality (ie killing additional birds to those which would normally die in a year) or compensatory mortality, whereby the harvest of shot birds is effectively produced from birds which would otherwise have died from other causes.

In most situations the reality is somewhere between these extremes. If strong competition for resources

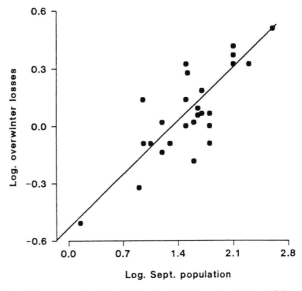

Figure 2.1 Density-dependent over winter losses in 35 inland mallard populations. At high population densities birds disperse or die whilst at lower population densities more ducks remain at a given site.

29

causes a higher percentage mortality at higher densities of mallard, the mortality is termed density-dependent. If shooting reduces competition by removing animals from the population, the *proportion* dying amongst those not shot will decrease, compensating to some degree for the numbers of birds shot. The quarry population should only be exploited at levels which it can sustain through the improved survival of unshot birds.

Hill's 1982 computer simulation model was based on long-term wildfowl counts from 35 inland waters kindly loaned by The Wildfowl and Wetlands Trust. The strongest phase of density-dependence occurred during the winter, when mallard in high density populations either died or dispersed more often than those in lower density populations. This relationship is described in the Figure 2.1.

The density-dependent relationship was built into a simulation model which produced the output for Figure 2.2. As can be seen from this figure, the calculated harvest rises up to a level of around 40% of the autumn population being shot, at which point it peaks. This is an example of the estimated maximum sustainable yield (MSY) in a population with very high breeding success and highly density-dependent winter loss. Above an exploitation of 40% the population is rapidly driven to extinction. Nowadays

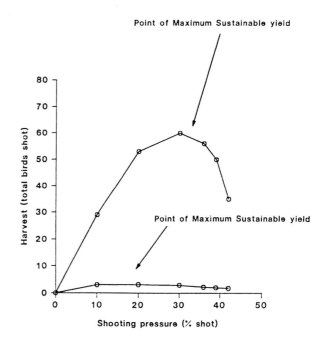

Figure 2.3 Computer simulation output of maximum sustainable yields from mallard populations with high duckling survival (upper line) and low duckling survival (lower line). Management practices which increase duckling survival can, it appears, greatly influence the potential yield of a population.

MSY levels are treated with a large degree of care and cropping well below them (at optimal sustainable levels of perhaps 20%) is normally recommended because natural fluctuations in quarry abundance from year to year means that the shootable bag will change. The figure does, however, illustrate the principle that duck populations can probably sustain quite severe levels of shooting mortality via compensatory increases in over-winter survival or re-distribution within the UK populations. In Hill's model the 40% MSY is achieved by maintaining the breeding population at 75% of that normally present without shooting. An exploited population of breeding birds will therefore be less abundant than an unexploited one provided the harvesting is sustained. This is in fact necessary to bring about the reduced competition and increased production of ducks each summer. If, however, heavy predation is occurring during the breeding season the predators may already be 'harvesting' the population at close to its maximum output and there will be no room for further harvesting. In this circumstance, predation control (killing foxes and corvids — crows and magpies — in the spring) allows greater production of birds, some of which will be available for shooting. Income derived from shooting can in turn be used to manage and conserve habitats in the long term. Thus the net effect of shooting with management is to increase, not lower, game stocks. The wise use of natural resources produces income for conservation. Many species of animal and plant benefit directly

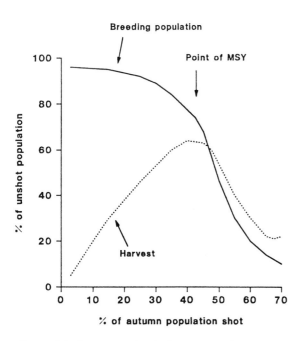

Figure 2.2 Computer simulation output of mallard populations which indicates that, in this example with very high breeding success and highly density-dependent winter losses, a maximum sustainable yield of around 40% can be stimulated by reducing the unshot population to 75% of its former density. In general, mallard populations could probably only sustain around 20% yield annually. Much more research is needed to provide accurate yield estimates.

from the conservation areas managed specifically for shooting.

Hill (1982) showed that for mallard, nest predation, duckling mortality and over winter loss can all act in a density-dependent manner – each form of adjustment in numbers giving scope for a potential harvest from the population. Increases in the proportion of ducklings surviving each breeding season (the upper line in Figure 2.3) can increase the potential yield from a (simulated) population.

Conservation costs money; waterfowl conservation is no exception, hunters are willing to pay for their sport and wildfowlers have provided a major impetus for the establishment of wetland reserves in Britain. Wildfowling does no damage to the conservation of waterfowl as long as the numbers of birds shot are carefully monitored and kept within the capacities of the various species to sustain the mortality due to shooting.

This mortality includes birds killed and those poisoned by lead shot. Disturbance of birds on feeding grounds could lead to reduced body condition and increased winter mortality, especially during very cold winters, but there is no published direct evidence to support the view that this effect is significant.

THE GAME CONSERVANCY
REVIEW OF 1988

Throughout the research, findings have been reported regularly in The Game Conservancy's Annual Review.

Wildfowling does no damage to the conservation of waterfowl as long as the numbers of birds shot are kept within sustainable limits.

Using our research at Great Linford on mallard and tufted duck we can now examine the features required for a productive duck breeding reserve.

Egg quality and the spring diet of mallard

Mike Birkhead showed in 1984 that large mallard eggs contain proportionately more yolk than smaller ones. Yolk is rich in fats and proteins and ducklings hatching from large eggs thus have larger food reserves and a better chance of survival than those hatching from small eggs. American and Scandinavian research has shown that a high protein diet, particularly one rich in invertebrates, is the key factor in a hen mallard producing good quality yolks. Pre-laying ducks can be fed through the winter on grain alone but they need a higher protein intake during the egg production period of the life cycle. Reserves managed to provide invertebrate-rich shallows close to nesting areas are likely, therefore, to be particularly attractive to nesting ducks. Mallard return to these areas with their ducklings to ensure that the young brood make the best use of food-rich habitats. Invertebrate-rich marshes, scrapes, pools and lake margins are highly beneficial both to pre-laying mallard and to young downy ducklings of 1 to 14 days of age.

In the early days at Great Linford it was felt that the reserve lakes lacked dense midge populations because of their apparently low productivity. Straw was chosen as an organic input to try and boost aquatic invertebrate production. Barley straw (*Hordeum sp.*) was added to six sites on the reserve in 1978 to simulate the input of dead leaf litter which natural lakes receive from reed stems and the like. (Street 1979). Straw initially caused a decrease in the numbers of chironomid midges emerging from experimentally treated areas, probably because it blanketed the lake bed and decreased the oxygen supply during decomposition. However, after this initial phase the invertebrate populations of the straw itself increased markedly and the technique does provide a boost to invertebrates in very immature lakes where a significant plant community has yet to develop under the water or round the shores.

Mike Street surfaces from the depths with an invertebrate mud core sample.

A further intriguing benefit of straw addition is the potential that the technique has for the control of algal blooms. Excessive algal growth in pools and small lakes can be controlled by the addition of loose straw bundles to inflowing streams. Leachates from the decomposing straw contain algistatic substances which suppress the growth of phytoplankton, clearing formerly 'pea green' pools plagued by algal blooms. To be fully effective, the water needs to be circulated through the straw either from inflow streams or via a pumping system.

Duck nesting success and the management of breeding habitat

Mallard search for suitable nesting sites in the early spring (February/March), whereas tufted ducks delay nesting until summer (June/July). Both species need to combine two fundamental aspects of habitat quality into their choice of breeding area: a 'safe' nest site; and high quality (ie food-rich) brood rearing habitat within reach of the nest site. Very young broods of ducklings will travel considerable distances (500m-1km), led by the duck, to reach rich feeding sites chosen prior to nesting. The ducks probably assess the quality of brood-rearing habitat during their active pre-nesting feeding when they search out the protein-rich invertebrate foods important for egg production.

'Safe' nest sites

David Hill (1981) showed that early mallard clutches suffered a higher predation rate (mainly from crows) than later ones and that the height of vegetation around the nest was a critical feature determining success or failure (Figure 2.4).

Tufted duck clutches also suffered higher predation rates when situated in low sparse cover. For both species, nesting success was higher on islands than on the mainland. This is probably related to reduced risks

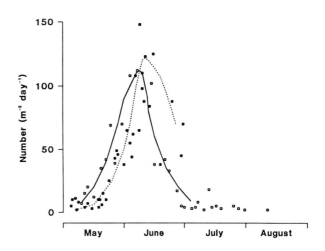

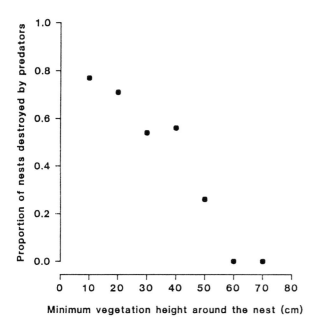

Figure 2.4 Crows predate a high proportion of mallard clutches where nests are in short vegetation. Well-hidden mallard nests in high vegetation have a high survival rate. Management of habitat to produce large blocks of rough grassland on islands gives waterfowl nests their best chance of success. Additional crow control may be necessary at some sites if maximum production of ducklings is the principal management aim.

from foxes and rats and, where islands have no trees for crows and magpies to scan the habitat, from corvid egg predators too. Mallard suffered more clutch losses than tufted ducks, probably due to their early nesting with generally poorer egg concealment. Mallard appear to 'accept' these early nest losses in order to time the peak duckling hatch to coincide with the peak chironomid midge hatches in May and June (Figure 2.5). Losses to egg predators usually occur during laying, when the duck visits the nest to lay the clutch over a two week period. Corvids in particular are likely to spot their coming and going.

Duck eggs are a favourite food of crows in spring.

Figure 2.5 Numbers of chironomid midges emerging per day on the Great Linford gravel pits. The solid and dotted lines refer to numbers of midges emerging from Main and St Peters lakes. Note how the emergence peaks in early/mid June when most ducklings hatch to take advantage of the food supply.

Chironomids are of key importance in the nutrition of young (less than 14 day) mallard ducklings. Young tufted ducklings can 'afford' to hatch much later (July or August) as they readily dive soon after hatching and have a much wider variety of invertebrate prey species available to them than the surface-bound mallard ducklings.

David Hill (1984) showed that the closer tufted duck nests were together, the greater the probability of predation. Density-dependent mallard nest predation was also demonstrated both at the Sevenoaks reserve in Kent and at Great Linford (Figure 2.6).

This poses a major problem for mallard conservation since the aim is to increase stock and therefore nest densities but this will lead to a higher *proportion* of clutches lost to predation. Successful encouragement of nesting therefore brings with it the need for high quality nesting habitat with thick tall cover (grasses, nettles, rushes, willowherb, etc.) and/or active spring

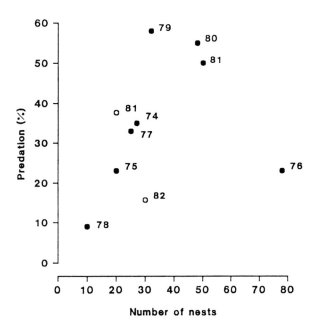

Figure 2.6 The proportion of total mallard egg clutches eaten by crows in a given year rises as the number of nests rises. This creates a management problem as successful reserves with large numbers of nesting ducks represent a 'honey pot' food supply for predators. Levels of predation need, therefore, to be controlled if maximum duck production is to be achieved.

Crows caught in a Larsen trap in spring.

predator control. The choice of whether to control foxes and crows in the spring/summer duck nesting period or whether to promote large areas of dense cover habitat and islands will vary from site to site depending upon local conditions.

Tufted ducks tend to cause management problems by aggregating nests into the most suitable areas of cover close to water on islands and thus providing 'honey-pot' feeding areas for egg predators. The best nesting islands occur in groups with well vegetated shorelines and in areas where potential predators are either naturally scarce or have been reduced. The

Mallard ducklings feeding in invertebrate-rich shallows.

situation of the Great Linford reserve, at the edge of the city of Milton Keynes, means that high numbers of foxes, crows and magpies living mainly in an urban environment, regularly raid the reserve to steal eggs and/or nesting ducks. This artifically high density of predators justifies the trapping of crows and the shooting of foxes to encourage higher levels of duck production.

Predation control

In our experience, predation of clutches of eggs by rats, crows and probably foxes and mink is a key factor limiting duck production on the unnatural habitat of restored gravel pits. Predation can be reduced in three ways:·

1. By providing well vegetated offshore nesting islands (no trees for crows to perch on) where both ducks and geese hatch off more clutches of eggs than from mainland nest sites.

2. By controlling crows and magpies (by Larsen trapping) rats and mink (in approved spring traps) and foxes during the critical 'window' (March – July) when most ducks nest. Advice on the humane control of predator numbers can be obtained from The Game Conservancy's Advisory Service (Telephone 0425 652381).

3. Small reserves and key nesting areas can be protected from foxes by high wire fencing and electrified barriers. However, wily individuals usually find a way in!

Brood-rearing habitat quality

Ducklings need plentiful supplies of protein-rich invertebrate food. Aquatic insects (especially non-biting chironomid midges, reed smuts and mayflies) and

Adult Chironomid Midge © Peter Gathercole

gastropod molluscs (aquatic snails) are all known to be important (Giles, unpublished). A safe nest site is often some distance away from a rich brood feeding site and as the overland distance which young ducklings need to travel increases so does their rate of mortality (Figure 2.7).

Figure 2.8 shows that, for both mallard and tufted ducklings, the sharpest phase of mortality occurs during the first two weeks of life, when aquatic invertebrates are especially important food items. After this time survival improves.

The ideal situation is to have islands covered in rough grass adjacent to rich, shallow, weedy shorelines. The ducklings then just need to hatch, dry out and waddle down to the shore for their first insect meal. For many years at Great Linford both mallard and tufted ducks nested in the reserve and then led their ducklings overland to the relatively distant River Great Ouse to feed. Mortality was high and the Wildfowl Reserve contained few duckling broods, indeed not enough to replenish those lost by natural mortality.

This long-standing situation was changed in 1988, after a large scale fish removal carried out during

Aquatic snail © Peter Gathercole.

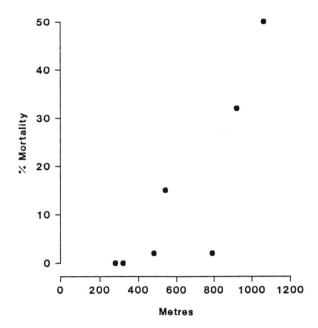

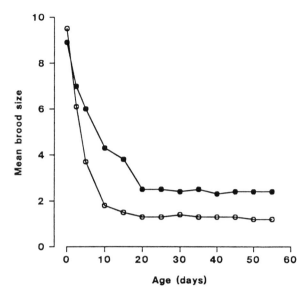

Figure 2.7 The percentage mortality of mallard broods increases with the distance which young ducklings have to move from the nest to their feeding grounds. Good reserve management, therefore, produces rich feeding habitat adjacent to high quality nesting habitat.

Figure 2.8 For both mallard and tufted duck, early research showed that most ducklings die during the first two weeks of life, during the phase when they need an abundant supply of aquatic insects for food. Recently, duckling survival for both species at Great Linford has increased substantially after the fish removal produced a surge in the availability of duckling food.

October/November 1987. The fish aspects of this work are discussed fully in Chapter 6; effects on ducklings are described here.

The survival of mallard and tufted ducklings tends to be very poor on gravel pit lakes compared with more natural habitats (Hill & Ellis, 1984, Hill *et al*, 1987). Poor downy duckling survival is restricted to the first two weeks post-hatching (Figure 2.8) during a phase of rapid growth and consequent high protein intake. Adult chironomid midges are an important component of this protein-rich food supply for both mallard (Street, 1977, Figures 2.9 and 2.10) and tufted ducklings. Aquatic snails and planktonic crustaceans are also very important for tufted ducklings (Lees & Street, 1973, Figure 2.11). The snail *Potamopyrgus jenkinsii* dominated the diet of young tufted ducklings at Great Linford. Larval chironomids are used as a food source by tufted ducklings in some habitats (Laughlin, 1973).

Mallard ducklings of 14 days of age or older tend to eat much more plant material than younger birds (Figures 2.9, 2.10), especially grass seeds which are available in large numbers. Once the ducklings reach this phase of development their subsequent survival is very good.

Street (1977) noted that mallard duckling mortality tends to be greatest after the peak of insect emergence which occurs each year in June. He suggested that the generally low invertebrate productivity of the Great Linford pits was due to their ecological immaturity.

However, subsequent fish removal studies have shown that predation on the invertebrate food supply by resident coarse fish was probably also important at this time of year.

The observations of young ducklings needing large quantities of animal protein to develop normally under natural conditions were followed up by laboratory experiments where mallard ducklings were reared on a range of diets incorporating increasing proportions of animal protein.

When mallard ducklings were reared in the laboratory on a range of diets to judge the relative dietary importance of plant seeds and invertebrates, birds given insect larvae grew much faster than those fed on either barley meal or a mixed seed diet. In fact a diet of at least 50% dry weight of insect larvae was needed before ducklings made any weight gain at all (Street, 1978). Duckling growth improves with both the proportion of invertebrates in the diet and with the total amount of animal protein eaten (Figure 2.12, Street 1978).

An adequate supply of insects to ensure good growth and survival of wild mallard ducklings (and the young of other duck species) thus seems essential.

Not surprisingly, mallard breeding appears to be timed to ensure that the peak duckling hatch coincides with peak insect emergence. After warm springs (February temperature) both mallard and tufted duck nest earlier

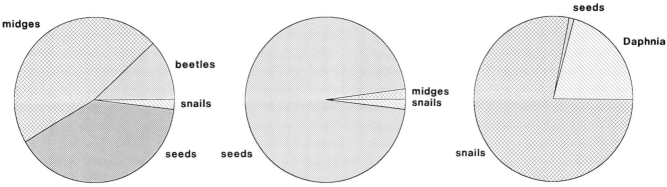

Figure 2.9 0-3 day old mallard ducklings at Linford were found to eat mostly aquatic midges and plant seeds. These young birds would not normally consume so much vegetable matter if the availability of insects on gravel pits was generally higher. Fish removal reduces the predation on aquatic insects to allow more flies to hatch at the water surface where young dabbling and diving ducklings feed.

Figure 2.10 12-24 day old mallard ducklings at Linford eat an almost completely vegetable diet of seeds. This is the normal situation for ducklings even at sites where aquatic insects are freely available. These older ducklings have survived the early phase of development when a high protein (insect) food supply is critical and they can now manage on a less protein-rich diet.

Figure 2.11 0-3 day old tufted ducklings at Linford rely almost entirely on a diet of aquatic snails. After the fish removal, Main Lake snail abundance increased greatly, much to the benefit of tufted duckling broods which started to feed on Main Lake and showed improved survival over previous years.

than in cold years. Also, the mean hatching date of mallard clutches was later in years when the date of peak chironomid hatch was late (Hill, 1984). The proportions of young mallard and tufted ducklings which survive to fledging are related to the abundance of aquatic midges available to them as a protein-rich food supply (Figure 2.13).

Scandinavian research supports this view. For example, on lake Myvatn in Iceland, several duck species time their duckling production to coincide with the enormous midge hatches. The observed poor duckling survival in the wild at Great Linford appeared to be related to low food availability (Street, 1977) and possibly to competition with fish for the available aquatic

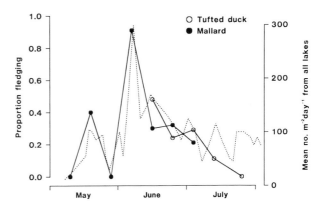

Figure 2.13 The proportion of both mallard and tufted duckling broods which fledge successfully is directly related to the average number of midges hatching from the lake surface at Great Linford. When midge availability is high, most ducklings survive to fledgling, when there are few flies it appears that most ducklings starve to death.

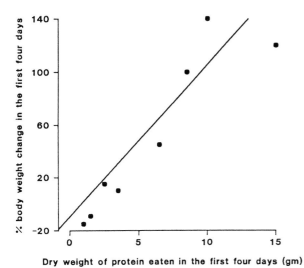

Figure 2.12 In laboratory experiments, mallard duckling growth rates during the first four days post-hatching were directly related to the amount of protein available in the diet. A high protein diet promotes rapid growth and development.

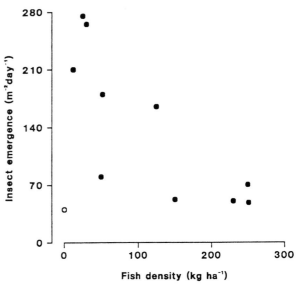

Figure 2.14 The emergence of insects on experimental ponds at Linford is directly related to the abundance of fish (bream and roach) present. High fish densities lead to low levels of insect production and, of course, to poor feeding habitat for ducklings.

Rosalind Wright in search of fish at Great Linford.

invertebrate food resource (Hill *et al*, 1987). On experimental ponds, the emergence of insects (midges and mayflies) was negatively associated with the abundance of fish (bream and roach, Figure 2.14).

Where does the ducklings' invertebrate food supply go?

Soon after gravel pits fill with water, female chironomids deposit egg masses on the water surface and the larvae hatch and distribute themselves widely in the newly forming lake. Pioneer chironomid species eke out an existence on a diet of algae and decaying organic matter (detritus). As the lakes develop a higher organic content in their sediments, the feeding conditions for the larvae improve and their populations become more prolific. Any fish entering the system (for example with winter floods, as at Great Linford) will prey on available aquatic invertebrates during their normal foraging behaviour. Fish of most species are very adaptable in their feeding biology and will switch from one abundant food source (eg *Daphnia*) to another (eg hatching insects) as they become available through the seasons and even at different times of day.

At Great Linford, the gravel pits were stocked naturally with coarse fish from the winter flooding of the adjacent River Great Ouse. The fish community was dominated by adult bream and roach, with numerous small perch, abundant predatory pike and low densities of carp and tench. A full analysis of the diets of the principal species is given in Giles *et al* (1990). Briefly, bream winnow lake bed sediments for chironomid larvae and small molluscs; roach eat either zooplankton (*Daphnia hyalina*), filamentous green algae, plant seedlings or organic detritus; perch specialise on chironomid pupae (preying on successive species as they emerge through the season) and tench eat a wide range of macroinvertebrates (Giles *et al* 1990). In Chapter 6 the role of fish as competitors for food with waterfowl is discussed fully. Suffice it to say here that in general, if a wetland complex is to be managed principally for waterfowl conservation, large

populations of adult coarse fish (especially carp, bream, tench, roach, rudd, perch and pike) are best removed. After fish removal, invertebrate populations increase (Chapter 6) and, in certain circumstances, aquatic plant growth also increases greatly. Both changes are of benefit to feeding wildfowl throughout the year.

Habitat use by tufted and mallard broods

During the late spring and summer of 1987, we systematically collected data on the distribution of tufted duckling broods at Great Linford and on the adjacent River Great Ouse (Figure 2.15). Main Lake was a relatively important habitat for mallard brood rearing. This lake has a much higher emergence of midges than the adjacent St Peter's breeding sanctuary where mallard broods were seen rarely.

Tufted ducks took their broods to an even more well defined rearing area; the slow flowing section of the River Great Ouse above Haversham weir (Figure 2.15). This crowding of tufted duckling broods into the very small area of habitat on the River Ouse was not a recent phenomenon at Great Linford, it had happened consistently in previous years. In 1987 we surveyed the section of river chosen by the ducks to try to discover the reason for its consistent popularity. Our survey showed an abundance of aquatic snails (100 per square metre) and also of pea mussels (*Sphaerium sp.*; 300 per square metre) associated with lily and reed beds growing in the shallower river margins. The tufted broods fed along the edges of the water lily beds. The water lily stems and leaves were covered with snails easily available to foraging tufted ducklings.

Use of Main Lake by tufted ducks with broods increased greatly between 1988 and 1990, after the fish removal

Tufted duckling picking snails from lily leaf.

carried out in October 1987. This increase in habitat use followed directly the increases in invertebrate foods stimulated by the fish removal. The use of the rest of the Great Linford site by tufted duck broods declined sharply as the use of Main Lake increased (Figure 2.16).

In a large aquarium, downy tufted ducklings readily dive for snails taken off aquatic plants, and for chironomid larvae from bottom sediments (Giles 1989). When the density of prey (chironomid larvae) is increased, the duckling's feeding success (number of larvae caught per dive) also increases linearly (Figure 2.17 and Giles, 1990).

The clear implication of these laboratory results is that when the natural food supply is increased (eg after fish removal), tufted ducklings forage more efficiently and potentially survive better than when the quality of the habitat is poorer (eg when fish are present).

Lees & Street (1973) have shown that tufted duck and their ducklings at Great Linford eat large numbers of aquatic snails. The post fish removal increases in snail

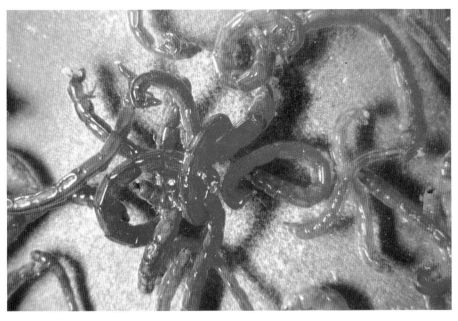

Chironomid larvae.

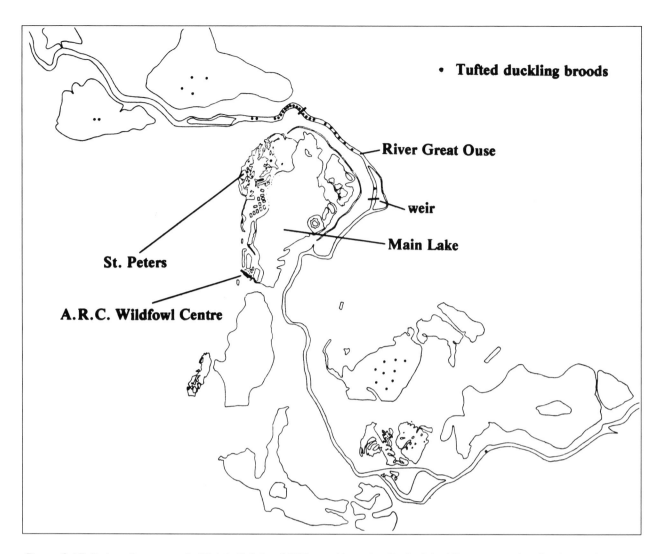

Figure 2.15 Before the removal of fish in October 1987, most broods of tufted ducklings were taken by the duck overland to the adjacent River Great Ouse, where the availability of aquatic snails was relatively high. The tufted ducklings fed mostly amongst the stems of water lily beds.

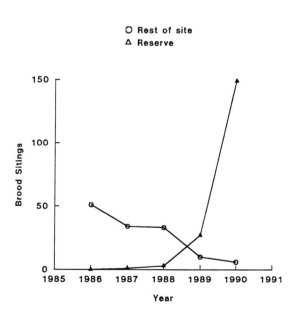

Figure 2.16 After the October 1987 fish removal, there was a mass movement of tufted duckling broods into the reserve and onto Main Lake, where food availability (especially snails and midges) had increased greatly.

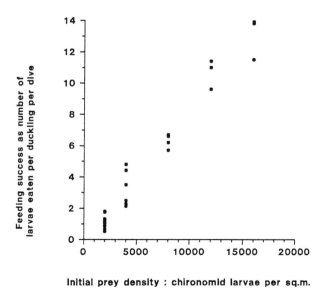

Figure 2.17 Laboratory experiments with tufted ducklings showed that these young birds catch more midge larvae per dive underwater as the availability of prey increases. This allowed us to predict that large-scale changes in food abundance in nature should lead to improved duckling growth and survival.

biomass in Main Lake (see Chapter 6) have probably been central to the increased habitat use and increased brood size at fledging recorded during the present study (Figure 2.18 and Giles, 1991).

Brood size of tufted ducks at fledging (Figure 2.18) appears to have increased from around three in 1986-87 when fish were present in the lakes, to around

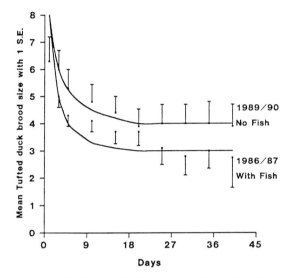

Figure 2.18 Tufted duckling brood size at fledging (a simple measure of average duckling survival) increased by around 33% after fish were removed from the Linford reserve lakes. More research is needed to see whether this improvement in survival is likely to be a permanent feature of the reserve.

four in 1989-90 after the fish removal. Survival has improved by around 33%. This interpretation assumes that the proportion of whole brood losses has not increased during the course of the study. More seasons of field data will be needed to assess whether the increase in survival is real and sustainable. Repeated attempts were made to radio track tufted ducks with broods to provide data on individual brood survival but the rate of nest desertion following capture and tagging was high, and the data were difficult to collect. Mallard are more amenable to such studies (eg Hill *et al* 1987). In addition to the post fish removal increase in use of the Wildfowl Reserve by tufted duck, mallard brood rearing use also increased (Wright & Philips 1990) and both shoveler, *Anas clypeata* and pochard, *Aythya ferina* have nested in the reserve and produced ducklings for the first time. In 1992, at the time of writing, these species have been joined by gadwall and ruddy duck – a significant increase in the diversity of duck species attempting to breed on the Linford reserve. In mid-June 1992 three broods of gadwall (with nine, six and four ducklings) were seen in the reserve – the first breeding recorded for this species at Great Linford.

Mallard

The response of mallard ducklings to the increase in the invertebrate food supply after fish were removed from Main Lake was studied across the whole of the Great

Table 2.1 Brood use of lakes at Great Linford 1989.

Lake (Area (ha) in brackets)	Lake Use	Fish Density	Number of Broods	Number per Hectare
Main Lake (16)	Wildfowl Reserve (fish removed)	v.low	6	0.37
St. Peter's (2)	Wildfowl Reserve (fish removed)	v.low	2	1.00
Stanton Low (1.8)	Managed water levels + fish removed	v.low	8	4.44
Total Reserve (19.8)		v.low	16	0.81
Trout Lake 1 (9.8)	Former trout fishery	low	4	0.41
Trout Lakes 2 and 3 (4.5)	Put & take trout fishery (regular removal of coarse fish)	low	5	1.11
Black Horse, Arboretum (12.5)	Coarse fishery	high	2	0.16
Dovecote (23)	Coarse fishery	high	2	0.09
Pond Spinney + Ditch (0.2)	Unstocked pond	v.low	2	10.00
Red House/Rocla (14.9)	Coarse fishery	high	4	0.27
Popular/Alder (4.3)	Carp fishery	high	0	0.00
River Great Ouse (7)		?	13	0.54
Averages				
Lakes with low fish density			27	39
Lakes with high fish density			8	0.13

Linford site. We were interested to see whether the ducklings tended to feed on areas of water where fish stock densities were low. Traditionally, mallard broods were mainly taken to the river Great Ouse for rearing, whilst medium numbers used the reserve Main Lake.

A considerable effort was made in 1989 searching for broods and identifying them from day to day. Even when the female was unmarked, this could be done by their age and location. Such methods, of course, lack the certainty of radio-tracking but useful information has been gained. Radio-tracking had been difficult due to malfunctioning transmitters.

The estimated numbers of broods seen on the different lakes on the site are shown in Table 2.1. It is apparent that the reserve had a high proportion of the total mallard broods in the area. In particular Stanton Low Lake seemed popular for brood-rearing. A large number of bream were removed from this lake in 1987, releasing the invertebrate food supply from fish predation. It is also subject to water level management which improves its productivity. In 1980 brood density in the reserve was recorded as 0.22 per hectare and in 1989 it was 0.81 per hectare, almost a four-fold increase. The River Great Ouse supported approximately the same density of broods (0.54 per hectare) as in 1980 (0.47 broods per hectare). The Trout Lakes are also used by mallard rearing their young; these lakes have a low density of coarse fish and the two are run as 'put and take' trout fisheries. The stock densities of trout in these lakes are fairly low and unlikely to affect insect abundance to any great extent.

The lakes which were poorest in the numbers of broods were those that are managed as coarse fisheries and have high fish populations. Alder and Poplar Lakes

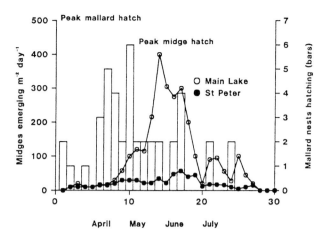

Figure 2.19 In 1989 most mallard clutches hatched too early (April/May) to take advantage of the peak midge hatch (May/June) and so, we believe, relatively few ducklings survived to fledging. It seems to be critical to get the insect supply to the ducklings at exactly the right time of year to promote optimal duckling survival.

are carp fisheries that have been heavily stocked; no ducklings were seen on these lakes. High stock density carp fisheries, which are becoming increasingly popular with anglers, tend to be very barren waters, both for waterfowl broods and for other wildlife.

Although nest density and the numbers of broods recorded were highest in the reserve in 1989, overall the number of ducklings surviving to independence was not noticeably higher than in previous years, although late hatching broods did very well.

Chironomid midge emergence was regularly monitored and, as in previous years, the peak hatch was in the first two weeks of June (Figure 2.19). The peak hatch of mallard, however, was in the first three

Mallard duck with large mature brood.

weeks of May, which meant that the majority of ducklings hatched too early to exploit the peak in the emerging chironomids. Mallard ducklings in their first 10 days of life need a high proportion of chironomids in their diet to survive. In 1989 there appears to have been a 'mismatch' between the hatching ducklings and peak chironomid emergence, probably because the extremely mild winter caused the mallard to lay early.

We estimate that in 1989 only 22% of mallard clutches hatched at the right time to take advantage of peak chironomid emergence. Further, although chironomid production has been much improved in the reserve by removing the coarse fish, it is still low compared to that of many nutrient-rich natural lowland wetlands. Therefore the timing of hatching for mallard at Great Linford may be extremely important as both before and after the peak emergence in June the numbers of chironomids emerging are very low (Figure 2.19).

Experimental work with tame mallard ducklings was undertaken to complement the observations of the wild broods. 30 minute feeding trials took place in a sheltered bay of Main Lake and a similar bay of Poplar Lake (a carp fishery). On release from their holding box, the ducklings rushed to the waters edge and began to forage actively. They always moved as a brood, changing their behaviour in unison. From the age of three days, on their first trial, the ducklings fed by sieving sediment in shallow water or by picking items from the surface. Their response to potential danger was also innate; they bunched close together, crouched and were silent. They reacted in this way to overhead herons (and aeroplanes!) and to approaching swans.

In these experiments the ducklings rarely gained weight; indeed on average they lost approximately 3% of their total body weight – a considerable amount in a period of only fifty minutes (trial time plus travel and drying time of about fifteen minutes). Their feeding efficiency was reduced by the sudden change in environment, restriction of feeding area and – probably most importantly – by the lack of a mother duck to lead them to profitable areas. However, comparison of pairs of trials on the two lakes revealed that those ducklings feeding on Main Lake (low fish density) consistently fared better than those on Poplar Lake (high fish density). Average weight losses were significantly less on the fish-free Main Lake. Ducklings also travelled less far during those trials. The average distance moved in a trial on Main Lake was 44m per half hour, compared with 58m on Poplar Lake. The ducklings on Poplar Lake also apparently abandoned feeding and spent some time clumped together, resting or preening in more than 70% of trials. This behaviour was much less common on Main Lake, where 60% of

trials were entirely devoted to foraging, and preening bouts were generally short.

Individuals of all the common aquatic invertebrate groups were present in both lakes. There were, however, major differences between them. There were 2.5 times as many *Asellus* (water louse) in the Poplar samples compared to those from Main Lake but the latter had five times as many oligochaete worms and 50 times as many chironomid larvae. The great difference in invertebrate densities in the two lakes can be largely attributed to the presence or absence of fish and probably explains the better performance of the ducklings in the trials on the fish-free Main Lake. This experimental work supported our observations suggesting that survival of mallard ducklings should be improved on lakes where food production has been increased by removing fish.

Table 2.2. Juvenile waterfowl recorded eating aquatic invertebrates (Giles, unpublished).

	Insects	Snails	Mussels	Crustacea	Other
Dabbling Ducks					
Mallard	X			O	O
Black duck	X	O	O	X	O
Blue winged teal	X	O		O	
Gadwall	X			X	O
Teal	X	O		O	O
Pintail	X			O	O
American wigeon	X	X		X	O
Shoveler	X				
Wood duck	X			X	
Shelduck	X				
Diving Ducks and associated groups					
Tufted	X	X		X	
Canvasback	X	X			O
Pochard	X				
Redhead	X			O	O
Lesser scaup	X	X		X	X
Great scaup	X			X	
Ring necked duck	X	X	X		X
Common scoter	X			X	
Velvet scoter	X	X			
Long tailed duck	X			X	
Barrows goldeneye	X	O		O	
Goldeneye	X			O	O
Ruddy duck	X			O	O
White headed duck	X				
Harlequin	X				
Common eider		X		X	
Steller's eider	X			O	
Hooded merganser	X				X
Red breasted merganser	X				
Goosander	X				
Red throated diver	X			X	
Dabchick	X				
Great crested grebe	O				
Slavonian grebe	X			O	O
Black necked grebe	X				

Key O = common, X = important

The 1991 data on mallard brood survival in the Great Linford reserve showed an average of 5.4 ducklings alive in broods of around 15 days of age – those having survived the difficult first two weeks during which invertebrate feeding is so essential. Prior to the fish removal, mallard broods in the reserve were often down to two or three ducklings at two weeks of age. Overall, then, there is evidence of a recent (post fish removal) improvement in duckling survival for both tufted and mallard broods using Main Lake at Great Linford.

A major reason for the worldwide breeding migration of waterfowl towards the poles may be to reach fish-free tundra pools which are insect-rich and ideal for duckling brood rearing. Tundra habitats are excellent feeding habitats in the spring and early summer. The universality of invertebrate feeding by ducklings and ducks can be seen in Tables 2.2 and 2.3.

Table 2.3. Adult waterfowl recorded eating freshwater and/or marine invertebrates (Giles, unpublished).

	Insects	Snails	Mussels	Crustacea	Other
Dabbling Ducks					
Wood duck	X			O	X
Mallard	X	O		O	X
Black duck	X		O	X	O
Blue winged teal	X	X		O	
Shoveler	X	X		X	
Pintail	X	O		X	O
American wigeon	X				
Gadwall	X			X	
Wigeon	X			O	O
Teal	X			O	O
Diving Ducks					
Tufted duck	X	X	X	X	
Canvasback	X	X	X		
Redhead	X	X		X	
Lesser scaup	X	X	X	X	X
Greater scaup	X	O		X	
Ring necked duck	O	O	X		
Goldeneye	O	O	O		
Ruddy duck	X	X	X		
Common scoter	X	O		X	
Velvet scoter			X		
Common eider		X	X		
Harlequin	X				

Key O = common, X = important

Increasing food supply for young ducklings

Since duckling survival is so critically linked to food availability, it is essential to ensure that wildfowl breeding sanctuaries have the following habitat freely available to broods of dabbling and diving ducks:-

Water depth should range from 50-300mm and the lake bed should be covered with a good mixed growth of submerged plants. Fish should be absent or netted out on a regular cycle to maintain high invertebrate availability for ducklings. The key invertebrate groups to encourage are midges and snails.

Changes in duck diet through their life cycle

When ducklings have completed their early (first two weeks) rapid growth and development phase, many species switch to a diet higher in plant material. Mallard and teal are examples of species which eat large quantities of plant seeds during the summer and autumn of their first year.

Table 2.4 shows how the diet of a wide variety of waterfowl varies seasonally. The importance of aquatic invertebrates during the spring and summer is evident in all groups. Diving ducks often also eat invertebrates as their staple diet during the autumn and winter.

The diet of fledged mallard varies tremendously through the year (Street 1975) as Figure 2.20 shows. Note the fundamental switch from invertebrates early in the year to vegetable matter in the autumn.

Table 2.4. Seasonal variation in dominant components of waterfowl diet (Giles, unpublished).

		Spring/Pre-Laying	Summer/Laying	Autumn/Winter
Dabbling Ducks				
Wood Duck	M		TP	TP
	F	AI	AI	AI/TP
Black duck	M		AI	
	F		AI	AI
Blue winged	M		AI	
Teal	F		AI	
Shoveler	M		AI	
	F		AI	
Mallard	F	AI	AI	AP/TP
Pintail	F	AI	AI	AI/TP
Gadwall	F		AP	AP
Wigeon			AI	AP/TP
Diving Ducks				
Tufted ducks		AI	AI	AI/AP
Canvasback	M	AP/AI		AI/AP
	F	AI/AP	AI/AP	AI/AP
Redhead	M	AP/AI	AP/AI	AP
	F	AP/AI	AP/AI	AP
Lesser scaup	M	AI/AP	AI/AP	AI/AP
	F	AI/AP	AI/AP	AI/AP
Greater Scaup			AI	AI
Ring necked duck				AI/AP
Goldeneye				AI/AP
Ruddy duck				AI
Common scoter			AI	AI
Velvet Scoter				AI
Long-tailed duck			AI	AI
Harlequin			AI	
Common eider				AI

Key AP = Aquatic plants
     TP = Terrestrial plants
     AI = Aquatic invertebrates
     TI = Terrestrial invertebrates
     M = Male, F = Female

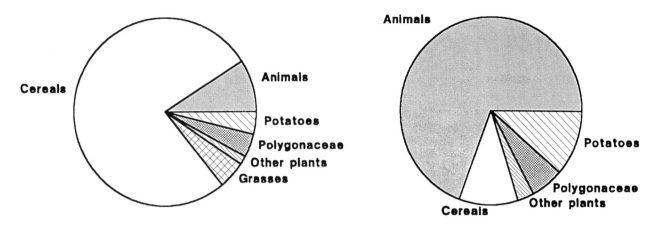

AUTUMN 1974

SPRING 1975

Figure 2.20 The autumn diet of adult mallard at Linford is largely cereals gleaned from harvested fields. In spring, adult mallard eat a high proportion of animal (aquatic invertebrate) food which provides a vital high protein intake prior to the breeding season.

The structure of the gizzard (an organ used to grind up tough food materials) also varies through the year, with the weight being highest (ie gizzard most muscular) in the autumn when the birds are feeding on cereal stubbles, and lowest in the spring when the birds switch to an invertebrate-rich diet prior to the breeding season.

Lead shot and the poisoning of wildfowl

When Mike Street analysed the diet of gravel pit mallard he found occasional lead shot in their gizzards. This aspect of our research has increasing international relevance because large numbers of wildfowl in the Mediterranean (eg around the Camargue) have been found to be poisoned by spent lead shot. The situation in Britain appears to be less extreme.

All waterfowl deliberately eat grit to aid the grinding action of the gizzard and both ducks and swans have been shown to suffer from fatal lead poisoning due to ingested shot. In the UK, in ducks, the shot usually derive from shotgun cartridges, whereas in swans angler's split shot are the usual source. In 1983 Mike Birkhead found that swans on the River Thames suffered 50% annual mortality due to ingested angler's weights. Non-toxic alternatives are now a legal requirement. Surveys of UK waterfowl containing lead shot showed high levels of ingestion by swans, mallard, pochard and tufted ducks, with lower levels in geese, teal, pintail, shoveler, wigeon and goldeneye (Birkhead, 1983). 8000 mallard are estimated to die from lead poisoning each year during the winter months.

There is agreement between conservationists and wildfowlers that the use of lead shot for wildfowling should be phased out in the near future in favour of non-toxic alternatives.

Conclusions: duck breeding ecology

The joint ARC/Game Conservancy research at Great Linford set out to increase the breeding success of mallard and tufted duck at the site and to shed light on waterfowl conservation generally. It quickly became apparent that the principal factors were correct nesting bahitat, low predation rates and invertebrate food for the ducklings. Throughout the project we have learnt more about how these key ingredients for duck breeding success can be supplied on a restored gravel pit site. Many of the lessons learnt have been of wider value to conservationists working in the field of wildfowl ecology.

CHAPTER 3

HABITAT MANAGEMENT FOR WADING BIRDS

Waders are those birds which belong to the order Charadriiformes. This group is defined by structural characteristics rather than by behaviour or habitat, and includes such diverse families as oystercatchers, plovers, sandpipers, curlews and snipe.

Many waders do wade, and have the long legs and long bills which are often thought of as typical wader characteristics. However some waders, for example plovers, seldom venture into the water. Conversely, many wetland birds such as herons, storks, cranes and ibises, which have long legs and bills and frequently wade, are not normally termed 'waders' by ornithologists.

The term 'shorebirds' has been used as an alternative name, but it is only really appropriate in areas such as the British Isles, where waders occur on migration or in winter. Most of the hundreds of thousands of waders which visit the estuaries and coasts of western Europe

in spring, autumn and winter spend the summer in the arctic and subarctic regions, where they often nest hundreds of miles from the sea. Even some species which may be seen in Britain all the year round are just as much at home in inland fields as they are on coasts and estuaries — lapwing and golden plover for example; by no means all birds seen on the shore are 'shorebirds' — a wide range of species from gulls to rock pipits regularly live by the coast.

Breeding waders in Britain

Of the sixty or so species of waders which have been seen in Britain, only about twenty regularly nest here, many in northern and upland areas (Table 3.1). The remaining forty occur only on passage or in winter, and of these about thirty are rare visitors.

Only seven species are at all common as breeding birds in lowland southern Britain. These are lapwing,

Table 3.1 Breeding waders in Britain

Species	Status in Britain
Lapwing	Common: throughout
Snipe	Common: throughout
Redshank	Coommon, but patchy
Oystercatcher	Common: coastal except in the north
Golden Plover	Common: moors in N and W Britain
Woodcock	Common: woodlands throughout
Curlew	Common, but scarce S and E England
Common Sandpiper	Common in N and W: upland streams, lakes
Ringed Plover	Common: scarcer and more coastal in S.
Little Ringed Plover	Fairly common: inland, England
Dunlin	Fairly common: upland moors
Greenshank	Scarce: N Scotland only
Dotterel	Rare: mountains
Whimbrel	Rare: Shetland, Hebrides and N Scotland
Black-tailed Godwit	Rare: wet meadows mostly E Anglia
Wood Sandpiper	Rare: Scottish bogs and moors
Ruff	Rare, wetland: mostly E Anglia
Avocet	Rare: coastal lagoons, mostly E Anglia
Red-necked Phalarope	Rare: Hebrides and Northern Isles
Stone Curlew	Rare: downland and heath, S and E England
Temminck's Stint	Very rare, Scotland

ringed plover, little ringed plover, snipe, woodcock, curlew and redshank.

Over the past few centuries, many lowland-breeding waders in Britain have relied for nesting upon various kinds of farmland managed in traditional ways. In more recent years these habitats have tended to disappear, or to be managed in new ways which are detrimental to the birds. Similarly, the estuaries and marshlands which provide important habitats for passage and wintering waders and other birds and wildlife have recently come under threat. While large estuaries and wetlands are irreplaceable and of international conservation importance, smaller areas of natural or artificial wetland may be managed or created to attract waders both during the breeding season and on passage. The new wetlands which come into being when mineral workings are flooded provide an opportunity for the creation of such habitat.

Species which have benefited from the increase in this kind of artificial wetland in Britain are those which nest in lowland riverine wet grassland (lapwing, redshank and snipe) or those requiring open, bare shingle or sand close to water (ringed and little ringed plovers, and also many oystercatchers. Street 1989). Most of the other native breeding species listed in Table 3.1 require highland, moorland or more specialised wetlands.

Lowland riverine wet grassland has become a scarce and diminishing habitat in recent decades and coastal shingle and sand is very much subject to disturbance from tourism, especially in southern Britain. The re-creation of these kinds of habitat wherever possible during the restoration of sand and gravel pits is therefore to be encouraged. It may not be possible to re-create exactly the natural system, but it is possible to produce habitat which is sufficiently similar to attract breeding waders.

At the ARC Wildfowl Centre at Great Linford, although the main emphasis since flooding took place has been on the creation of habitats for wildfowl, all the British breeding waders which readily take to restored mineral workings have bred except for the oystercatcher.

Sand and gravel nesters

Ringed and little ringed plovers are rather similar in appearance and in nesting habitat requirements. Both have short bills and rather short legs, and are examples of waders which do not really wade. They feed on small insects on land, and mud-dwelling invertebrates at the water's edge.

Ringed plover

The British Isles and Brittany form the south-western limit of the ringed plover's world breeding range. In this region it was primarily a coastal breeding species, although it has also always nested along rivers and by lakes, for example in Scotland and northern England. In the Arctic tundra, on the other hand, inland breeding is common.

In Britain, the coastal beaches which formerly provided breeding habitat for most ringed plovers have become very vulnerable to human disturbance this century, and since the 1950s ringed plovers have shown an increasing tendency to nest inland. Those which have remained at the coast have increasingly tended to nest within power station and oil refinery compounds or on farmland close to sea walls. Particularly in England, ringed plovers take readily to artificial inland sites such as reservoirs, gravel pits and other man-made or modified habitats, although they are not quite such characteristic gravel pit birds as little ringed plovers. The United Kingdom population of ringed plovers has recently been estimated as about 8600 pairs, with 1200 pairs at inland sites, mostly gravel pits (Andrews & Kinsman 1990). Artificial sites therefore provide a significant proportion of ringed plover breeding habitat in Britain.

Little ringed plover

Over much of its European range the little ringed plover is the inland counterpart of the more coastal ringed plover, nesting traditionally on shingle beds along rivers. Unlike the ringed plover it is a summer visitor to Britain, spending the winter in Africa.

Unknown as breeding birds in the British Isles until 1938, little ringed plovers were formerly very rare, even as passage migrants; they are still rare in Ireland. In 1938 a pair nested on a reservoir at Tring, Hertfordshire; in 1944 there were two pairs at Tring and one pair in Middlesex. Subsequently there was a

Little ringed plover chick.

steady increase to over 400 pairs by 1972 (Sharrock 1976). The species is still rare enough to be given complete protection under Schedule 1 of the Wildlife and Countryside Act of 1981, making it an offence to disturb the birds at or near the nest.

More recently the population has been estimated at up to about 650 pairs, all inland and the vast majority at gravel pits, but also at industrial tips, waste ground, sewage farms, reservoirs, and a few in natural river habitats. They have also shown an increasing tendency to use artificial sites on the Continent in recent years (Andrews & Kinsman 1990). The increase in Britain was caused by the increase in gravel pits.

Habitat for ringed and little ringed plovers

The breeding habitat requirements of the two small plovers overlap considerably and there may therefore be competition for breeding space between the two species. Ringed plovers can drive off and displace the smaller little ringed in areas where suitable habitat is limited.

Although they will use sparsely vegetated areas, the usual ringed plover nest site is on an open beach or shingle bank. Similarly, little ringed plovers usually make an exposed nest on gravel, although they will sometimes nest on sand, silt or dried mud.

Both plovers are therefore most likely to be attracted by large areas of exposed low-lying unvegetated shingle or gravel (minimum area about 0.2 hectare) close to water. Both appear to prefer substrates with a range of particle sizes, and in creating nesting habitat it is advantageous to include some fine pea-gravel or sand. Shingle beaches designed as loafing banks for wildfowl often provide suitable nesting habitat. The well-camouflaged eggs are laid in a simple scrape on the bare ground.

Both species, especially little ringed plovers, tend to be early colonists of new mineral workings and will breed close to an active operation. Such habitats tend to be fairly disturbed, but the birds appear tolerant of disturbance and will readily lay up to four repeat clutches if the first nests of the season are taken by predators or destroyed by sheep or cattle. The proportion of unsuccessful clutches even in natural situations is generally high, due to predation by both birds (crows and magpies for example) and mammals (especially foxes, but also mink in some areas).

Ringed plovers require shallow water very close to the nest site but little ringed are apparently more flexible and will lead their newly-hatched chicks distances of up to several hundred metres from the nest to the water's edge, where they do most of their feeding. For both species, the chicks' feeding areas should be kept free from marginal vegetation to allow them unimpeded access to the shoreline.

Little ringed/ringed plover nesting habitat.

To retain bare unvegetated gravel or shingle banks or islands at artificial sites, regular maintenance is necessary. Physical 'weeding' of plants during September to March and the application of herbicide may be necessary, while winter flooding with a draw-down during March, may be used to mimic the effects of seasonal flooding of the gravel river beds which are the natural equivalent of this habitat. The need for maintenance may be reduced if during the initial construction of nesting sites the gravel is spread onto a layer of plastic to a depth of a few centimetres. Plant growth will be retarded because roots cannot penetrate to the underlying soil. This method may however only be used on level sites where the gravel will remain in place.

Plovers are ground nesters and vulnerable to mammalian predators like foxes, hedgehogs and rats, so islands or floating rafts often provide the safest nesting sites. Artificial islands should be surfaced with shingle and ideally project only a few centimetres above the surface of the water. There should be sufficient shoreline to allow the newly-hatched chicks to obtain food. Such island sites are also likely to attract nesting common terns if there is suitable feeding habitat with plentiful fish nearby.

Grassland waders – lapwing, snipe and redshank

Lapwing

Lapwings were formerly common on farmland, nesting in permanent pasture, ploughland and (in March and April, when the first eggs are laid) young corn. These days lapwings are less common on farmland in the south of Britain and the decline may be attributed to changes in agricultural practice. Examples include the conversion of pasture to arable land, drainage of damp meadows, reclamation of waste ground, and especially the change to autumn sowing of cereals. In the north of Britain, by contrast, there has been an increase in numbers (Sharrock 1976). In many southern localities most lapwings now breed on marginal land, for example near gravel pits, sewage works or refuse tips. Dwindling areas of damp permanent pasture are becoming increasingly important.

Lapwings will nest in a wide range of relatively dry habitats but usually feed – and chicks especially – on open moist areas with short vegetation or patches of bare ground. The nest itself varies from a simple scrape at dry sites to a substantial saucer of grass and straw, and is usually situated on an exposed elevation such as a mossy hummock, old ant-hill, flattened tussock or ridge between furrows. Adult birds feed mostly on earthworms, but surface-living insects, particularly ground beetles, are also frequently taken. Dung-associated insects can be important in drier situations. Most feeding takes place within 100-300 metres of the nest and most nests are fairly close to water, where feeding is best. Eggs are laid in late March and early April in the southern lowlands, later further north and at higher altitudes. Four eggs are normally laid in each clutch. The newly-hatched chicks begin to feed themselves straight away on invertebrates which are taken off the ground or from low vegetation. Chicks from nests on arable land are often led by their parents to damp pastures, or gravel pits if such habitat is available nearby. Lapwings are very noisy and demonstrative in defending their nests and young, sometimes attempting to lure intruders away by feigning a broken wing.

The British breeding Lapwing population was recently estimated at just over 200 000 (Andrews & Kinsman 1990), and a relatively small proportion breeds at flooded gravel pits.

Lapwing: in decline but benefitting from restored gravel pit habitats.

Snipe

Of all the lowland waders, snipe are the most dependent upon wet ground for nesting. Their very long bills are adapted for deep probing into soft, wet ground. Although they are sometimes found in dry meadows, more typical nesting sites include rushy fields, water meadows, washes, bogs, saltmarshes and marshy edges of rivers and lakes (Sharrock 1976). The nest is often well-hidden in a tussock of grass or sedge, usually in a relatively dry part of the breeding territory.

Snipe have declined in many areas of Britain, especially in the south, due to changing agricultural practices, particularly land drainage. The British population was estimated to be about 30 000 pairs in 1986 (Piersma 1986), a noticeable decrease from around 100 000 pairs in 1972 (Sharrock 1976).

Due to their more exacting requirements, snipe are less common than the other waders as breeding birds at flooded gravel pits.

Redshank

With their long legs and long bills, redshank are characteristic 'waders'. Their usual breeding habitat is damp (but not very wet) marshland, wet pasture and other damp grassy or rushy fields, generally with little or no lush vegetation. The old name, 'watchdog of the marshes', derives from the birds' habitat and their noisy, 'yelping' alarm calls when disturbed. Inland redshank feed on small insects and aquatic invertebrates picked from the water surface and vegetation in shallow water at the edges of pools and ditches. They enter the water much more readily than the lapwing and snipe which may occupy the same habitat, and are true 'waders'.

In 1986 it was estimated that there were about 30 000 pairs of redshank in the British Isles, which is around 20% of the European breeding population (Piersma 1986). Numbers may vary considerably from year to year, depending on mortality during cold winter weather, to which redshank seem particularly vulnerable.

Inland breeding has declined considerably in recent decades, largely due to habitat changes – particularly land drainage. The distribution in southern Britain is now noticeably concentrated around the coast, and nearly 60% of the population nests in saltmarshes. Redshank are more common in northern Britain, where habitat changes have been less marked.

In southern England in particular, flooded gravel pits have provided very good breeding habitat in recent years, although at unmanaged sites the conditions are only temporarily suitable before muddy and grassy areas become overgrown with tall vegetation.

The nest is often made in a prominent tussock of grass or sedge, and the vegetation around the nest is usually about 0.2m high (taller than that chosen by lapwing, but shorter than for snipe). Egg laying peaks in May; four eggs are laid and there is a single brood. Incubating birds may feed up to 1.5km from the nest. The newly-hatched young will follow their parents to shallow water where they can immediately begin to feed themselves.

Habitat requirements of grassland waders

While shingle-nesting waders always need to be near open water when nesting, the grassland species are not dependent on open water or its associated vegetation. However, the greatest breeding densities nevertheless occur where the water table is high (Fuller 1982). This is probably because the birds' invertebrate food is either less abundant or less accessible in dry conditions. Patches of standing water make grassland more attractive to breeding waders in spring, especially redshank. Wet ground appears to be less important for lapwings than for redshank and snipe. Damp feeding areas may be important for the survival of young chicks, which have to begin to feed themselves immediately after hatching.

Grassland waders are more likely to choose less disturbed sites, with level and extensive aprons of short vegetation close to water, and with feeding areas consisting of low lying muddy spits, islands, or scrapes lined with topsoil. If these feeding sites are allowed to vegetate over, waders will no longer use them. In addition, redshank will be attracted to nest in marshy or damp areas, ponds, and damp tussocky grassland (ideally a few hectares). Snipe need open feeding areas, of a minimum size of about one to two hectares, preferably with areas of exposed mud. The site should provide shelter from the wind, ideally in the form of belts of reeds, iris or other vegetation in a 'chessboard' pattern, but too much cover is detrimental.

Where feasible, grazing by sheep or cattle in late summer is the best method of maintaining an optimum sward height and structure, preventing invasion by woody plants. Grazing by cattle will have the additional beneficial effect of promoting tussocks for nesting. Grazing in late summer may also improve habitats for snipe; trampling breaks up the surface of the soil and cattle dung attracts invertebrates. Intense grazing should not however take place between April and early June when waders are nesting.

If some allowance can be made during the restoration of gravel pits for fluctuation in water levels, regular winter flooding with a March draw-down may be used to prevent rank vegetation from becoming established. It may prove necessary to use a herbicide such as glyphosate from time to time in conjunction with flooding or grazing. Colonisation of damp grassy areas by rushes is very likely to occur and these too may need to be controlled with herbicide.

Features of breeding wader habitat

Key features to aim for in creating successful breeding habitat for waders are: nesting sites (gravel/shingle or suitable grassland) and shorelines with banks graded as gently as possible (providing broad areas of shallow water and damp, muddy margins) and with convoluted edges (providing as great a length of shoreline as practicable, with sheltered bays and spits). In shallow water sunlight penetrates to the bed, stimulating plant growth and forming the basis of a productive food chain. It is advantageous therefore to make the bank gradient very gentle right down to the deeper water, so that there are always shallow areas even when the general water level drops. Shorelines are best over-excavated during construction, allowing 0.2-0.3m of topsoil to be placed onto the sand or gravel substrate; this will result in improved productivity and better feeding conditions for waders. Wildfowl will also benefit from these features.

Some scattered small patches of vegetation are useful as cover for chicks to hide in, but rank vegetation should not be allowed to develop within 100m or so of the shallow water. Trees or woody vegetation are generally undesirable because crows use trees as lookouts. Mammalian predators may conceal themselves in scrubby growth and there should be as little vegetation fringing the water as possible.

Lack of disturbance by people, dogs, and machinery between April and July is also important, more so for the grassland waders than for the small plovers. The proportion of unsuccessful ringed and little ringed plover clutches is generally high due to predation by both birds and mammals.

Disturbance and predation may both be minimised by providing vegetated nesting islands.

Breeding waders at the ARC Wildfowl Centre

At Great Linford, restoration following the completion of extraction involved the creation of undisturbed lakes and ponds with grassy surrounds, shallow margins and long shores. Other features include shingle loafing areas (designed for wildfowl) and more recently a broad bund, kept free of rank vegetation by winter flooding, where shallow pools remain into the breeding season. A good population of nesting waders has built up in these habitats, particularly on the bund, which is deliberately isolated from each shoreline by deep water channels to exclude foxes.

Little ringed plovers were already nesting while extraction work was still proceeding. Since restoration, up to three pairs of little ringed and four pairs of ringed plovers have nested annually. Despite the general preference of both species for gravel and shingle, in recent years nests have been made on the hard mud surface of the bund. There has also been a tendency for ringed plovers to increase at the expense of little ringed.

Lapwing numbers have tended to increase since the site was flooded, and in 1991 seven pairs were counted within the reserve.

In 1992 nine lapwing broods were present in late May, all on the long bund in Main Lake. The soil level was just below the water surface, maintaining an ideal wet brood-rearing area. Redshank, little ringed plover and ringed plover were all present nesting on the bund at the same time.

Snipe bred in 1973 (very soon after restoration, when areas of muddy ground may have provided good habitat), and in 1990 a pair was present during the nesting season and breeding displays were seen, although breeding was not proved.

Undisturbed wet grassland, shallow pools and muddy margins have proved suitable for up to six pairs of redshank in recent years. Linford is one of only three breeding sites in Buckinghamshire for this declining but attractive wader.

Passage waders

Every year many thousands of waders travel through the British Isles on their way between breeding areas to the north and east and wintering grounds in Africa. Thousands more come to spend the winter here. The numbers of most British nesting species involved in these migrations are far in excess of the small British breeding populations. Many are concentrated at major estuaries and coastal wetlands where huge flocks congregate. However, migrating waders regularly pass overland and if suitable habitat is available they may drop in at inland sites to rest and feed, often only staying for a few hours. Although individual sites may have rather few species and numbers may be comparatively small, the total for all such sites in Britain is considerable and the provision of habitat for passage waders may make a positive contribution to their conservation (Andrews & Kinsman 1990). The best sites can record twenty or more species in a single year.

In general, the waders most likely to be seen on migration at inland gravel pit sites are the marshland species such as green sandpiper and greenshank, or those which will use a wide range of feeding habitats, such as dunlin and common sandpiper. However, predominantly estuary-feeding waders (knot and bar-tailed godwit, for example) may be seen from time to time, and even coastal waders such as turnstone, which usually inhabit rocky shores and tidelines, and sanderling, usually seen on sandy beaches, sometimes put in an appearance.

Active gravel workings with shallow pools, wet ground and sparse vegetation, provide habitat for nesting plovers and redshank and are also suitable for passage waders. Immigrant lapwing flocks for example gather at wetlands, including active gravel pits, from late summer onwards. However the habitat provided by active pits is temporary and shifting. Control of vegetation and water levels are required to perpetuate this type of habitat in the absence of active workings. Also, the highly inorganic nature of the mineral substrate at gravel workings often means that wet areas — especially temporary pools — tend to be biologically unproductive, with little invertebrate food for waders.

Habitat features which will benefit breeding waders and also wildfowl are likely to attract migrating waders as well. All these birds will benefit from areas of marshy ground, open mud and sand, ponds, long wavy shorelines, shallow bays, and promontories. Lack of disturbance is also important.

A drawn-down lake exposing mud for waders

Ideal is a network of small shallow pools at different levels with respect to the water table, which will flood and dry seasonally so that at least some suitable habitat is always available. However, accurate prediction of final water levels is essential during the construction of such a system. Water level control using sluices may be a preferable technique because it allows fine control and is less dependent on rainfall or levels in feeder streams.

As with nesting wader habitat, land plant growth should be kept to a minimum along the water's edge to maximise areas of mud, allow birds access and provide them with good views of the surroundings in case of predators or disturbance by people. Migrant redshank and snipe will tolerate a certain amount of vegetation but others, especially estuarine species, prefer shorelines to be as open as possible. The same techniques of grazing, flooding, herbicide and/or physical control which apply to breeding habitats may be used.

Ditches with some open 'edge' in the form of a shelf approximately level with the spring or autumn water level will attract green sandpipers in particular. If cattle are allowed access to the shore in places they will create boggy conditions suitable for snipe. Cattle should not however be allowed to get to the whole length of shoreline as they will cause over-enrichment through manuring and may completely remove desirable water plants (Street 1989).

When not feeding, waders spend their time 'loafing' (sleeping, resting, and preening), often in undisturbed areas near feeding sites. Loafing waders (and also gulls and waterfowl) prefer banks with a very short grass sward or areas of almost bare gravel beach immediately next to open water. South-facing sites sheltered from the wind are ideal.

At Great Linford, a water regime was introduced in 1985 on a 2ha lake (Stanton Low) with the aim of improving the site for feeding waders, and also to

Redshank: common at Great Linford.

improve duck breeding success. The water level at this lake is controlled using sluices. Levels can be progressively reduced by a few centimetres at a time.

The lake is completely flooded in early spring, surrounding five islands (used by nesting ducks) with water and making them secure against predators and disturbance. The rising water reflooding the lake bed creates a good feeding site for ducks. The water level is held at the level of the bank top throughout the nesting period, and then a very gradual draw-down is initiated in mid-July. The lake bed gradient is very gentle and large areas of mud are exposed by a small drop in water level. The local ducks, lapwings, ringed and little ringed plovers and redshank are quickly attracted to the exposed mud. In early autumn, the first autumn passage waders start to arrive, often including green sandpipers.

When draw-down is complete, towards the end of the autumn, the lake stays almost empty, with large areas of bare mud and much shallow water. Oxidation and mineralisation of plant material is speeded up by exposure to the air, making nutrients available at the lowest levels of the food chain. In spring when the lake is flooded again, aquatic organisms which have overwintered in the limited areas which have remained flooded can quickly recolonise and take advantage of these nutrients. The result is to increase the amount of food available to birds.

From summer to early autumn 1985, the numbers and species of waders using Stanton Low during the autumn draw-down were monitored daily (Street 1986). Water levels and the numbers of waders present are summarised in Figure 3.1 and Table 3.2.

The outlet sluice was first opened on 8 July and the level allowed to fall until 24 July, by which time it had dropped by 0.32m. Numbers of waders increased

Wet mud for feeding waders

Research at Great Linford has shown that the one feature above all others which attracts migrating waders, whatever their usual habitat, is the presence of areas of wet mud. Marshy areas, with pools and wet grassland, are also attractive, but the presence of mud is paramount. If areas can be provided where water can be gradually drained off a very gently sloping shoreline over a long period, leaving the mud exposed, waders will concentrate here. Ideally, exposed mud should be present during the Spring and Autumn wader passage (April and May and mid-July to mid-September).

Table 3.2 Numbers of waders at Stanton Low in autumn 1985 in relation to water level.

Date	Mean number of waders present per day	
	Water level falling	Water level stable
8.7 - 24.7	16	
25.7 - 5.8		13
6.8 - 19.8	18	
20.8 - 27.8		14
28.8 - 7.9	17	
8.9 - 30.9		9
Overall mean waders present	17	11

quickly as soon as the levels began to fall. The species attracted included green sandpiper, redshank, little-ringed plover, ringed plover, dunlin, common sandpiper, black-tailed godwit, turnstone and lapwing. The level was then held stable for twelve days, during which time the numbers of individuals and species of waders fell. The decrease began as soon as the water level stabilised (see Figure 3.1).

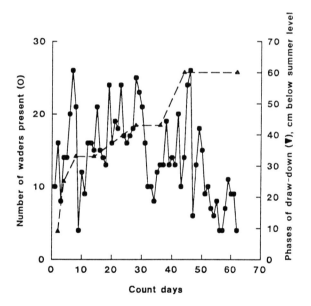

Figure 3.1 The number of wading birds counted on Stanton Low tends to be higher immediately after a phase of lowering the water level to expose wet mud. After the mud has dried out the birds tend to disperse until the water is lowered again, when a fresh influx of migrating waders occurs.

On 5 August the sluice was re-opened so that the water level could begin to fall once more. Again, numbers of waders began to increase immediately and numbers remained high until 19 August when water levels again stabilised. Further wader species attracted included common snipe, greenshank, little stints, whimbrel, ruff and curlew sandpiper. Only eight birds of five species remained on 25 August.

From 27 August to 7 September levels were allowed to fall again. By now 60% of the lake was mud and the water was 0.60m below the summer level. Numbers and diversity again increased, with a peak of 26 birds of seven species on 7 September. Numbers of waders then decreased once more as the autumn passage tailed off during stable water levels, but in this and other years notable concentrations of wigeon and especially teal began to build up at the lake from the end of autumn onwards.

It was clear from this study that wading birds were attracted by exposed mud and very shallow water during falling water levels. Numbers and variety of species increased while water levels were falling and decreased while levels were stable, even though there was still exposed mud. It seems that migrating waders are attracted by areas of *wet* mud while the water is receding. Waders flying over at a considerable height are probably able to recognise wet mud from its shiny surface, which perhaps produces a similar effect to conditions at an estuary while the tide is ebbing. While water levels are stable, the exposed mud dries quickly in the open air, the birds' invertebrate food becomes less available and at the same time the mud is less visible from a distance.

This study showed the importance of achieving very fine control over water levels if freshwater wetland is to be managed for migrating, as well as nesting, waders. The aim should be always to have visible, shiny, newly-exposed areas of wet mud.

Non-breeding waders at the Wildfowl Centre

The species of waders which have occurred at Great Linford in recent years are listed in Table 3.3. The table shows that the species which breed here also occur as migrants, and it is often difficult to distinguish passage birds while the summer breeding population is still resident.

'Frequent' species in the table were recorded in five or six out of the eleven years, usually less than ten individuals in any year. 'Occasional' species were recorded in three or four out of the eleven years, usually less than four per year when recorded.

Most of these waders breed in Eurasia and are fairly common on passage in Britain. Wood sandpipers, curlew sandpipers and little stints are less common. Pectoral sandpipers are scarce, though annual, visitors from North America, mainly to coastal sites in Britain: the Linford bird was seen feeding on the exposed mud of Stanton Low.

The remaining thirty or so species of waders on the British list are mostly rare visitors from Eurasia or North America. Any one of them could conceivably occur at Great Linford and similar sites.

Table 3.3 Waders at Linford 1981 to 1991

Species	Preferred Habitat on passage	Linford status
Lapwing	farmland, estuaries	common (winter)
Golden Plover	farmland, estuaries	annual (winter)
Snipe	wet ground	annual (winter)
Dunlin	most wetland	annual, common
Redshank	most wetland	annual, common
Common Sandpiper	most wetland	annual, common
Ringed Plover	seashores, estuaries	annual, common
Little Ringed Plover	freshwater; marsh etc	annual, scarcer
Green Sandpiper	pools, marshes, creeks	annual, up to 25
Greenshank	marshes, estuaries	annual, up to 20
Ruff	marshes, estuaries	annual, 5-10
Curlew	farmland, estuaries	annual, up to 6
Spotted Redshank	estuaries, marshes	annual, up to 4
Woodcock	woodland	annual, 1-2 winter
Black-tailed Godwit	marshes, estuaries	frequent, few
Whimbrel	estuaries	frequent, few
Curlew Sandpiper	estuaries, marshes	frequent, few
Oystercatcher	mainly coastal	occasional
Turnstone	coasts, estuaries	occasional
Little Stint	estuaries, marshes	occasional
Sanderling	beaches, estuaries	occasional
Wood Sandpiper	marshes, pools	occasional
Bar-tailed Godwit	estuaries, coasts	occasional
Jack Snipe	wet ground	occasional
Knot	coasts, estuaries	two: 1987, 1988
Grey Plover	estuaries, coasts	four in 1990
Pectoral Sandpiper	marshes, estuaries	one in 1989
Grey Phalarope	oceanic	one in 1987

CHAPTER 4

HABITAT MANAGEMENT FOR WINTER WILDFOWL

More than one million wildfowl are usually present in Britain in winter. Our relatively mild climate provides good conditions, with only short periods when wetlands are frozen or snow covered. Some species, for example eider, long-tailed duck, and the scoters, are restricted to salt water. Brent geese are coastal, whilst ducks like wigeon and pintail winter on the coast or in estuaries in large numbers but are also found inland. The majority, nevertheless, prefer freshwater habitats away from the shore.

However, over the centuries large tracts of inland and estuarine marshes, fens and lowland flood meadows have been drained for agriculture. More recently the creation of lakes as ornamental features, reservoirs or as a result of mineral extraction or mining subsidence has mitigated against this extensive loss. Man-made wetlands are increasingly valuable to wildfowl wintering in Britain.

Figure 4.1 National Wildfowl Count data (re-drawn from Owen *et al*, 1986) shows how the numbers of wildfowl wintering on gravel pits has increased steadily in recent years.

Gravel pits as habitat for wildfowl in winter

Central and southern England has few natural lakes, though some man-made waters are very old, for example the Norfolk Broads are flooded peat diggings dating from the 14th century. In the 20th century, however, there has been a dramatic increase in the number of lakes resulting from mineral extraction, the majority of which are flooded gravel workings in lowland river floodplains. Figure 4.1, which uses National Wildfowl Count data (Owen *et al*, 1986) shows the increasingly influential role of these lakes in the distribution of wildfowl in winter in Britain. Approximately 10% of the wildfowl counted in the early 1980s were on gravel pits. As most gravel pit lakes are in southern Britain their importance in this region is even greater.

Conflicts with recreation

Many gravel pits are close to urban areas and there can be a conflict between the interests of nature conservation and recreational uses. There is considerable overlap in the sites most suitable for wildfowl and for water sports. Most wildfowl arriving in Britain in winter from the far north are unfamiliar with people and are easily disturbed. The degree of susceptibility to disturbance varies from species to species and the more wary require large areas of quiet, open water. Studies by English Nature and the Sports Council (Tuite, 1982; Watmough, 1983) illustrated the problems. Water-bourne sports, especially those involving powered craft, are disturbing to wildfowl, whilst bankside activities such as angling, dog-walking or merely birdwatching can be disruptive.

Lake size and shape affect the degree to which wildfowl populations and recreation can co-exist. On large waters, careful zoning of activities can successfully reserve quiet areas for wildlife. Where chains of lakes exist, the birds will move from one to another

Undisturbed wetland habitat is hard to find in Southern England.

when disturbed, using those designated solely as wildfowl refuges for most of their activity. However, repeated disturbance still has a cost to the birds in terms of lost feeding time and extra energy expended on movement.

At Great Linford, the wildfowl move freely between the lakes, with the greatest use concentrated away from the coarse fishery. The reserve lakes and the southern Trout Lake (10ha, with low fish populations and no recreational use) are most popular. Haversham Lake is also attractive though frequented by anglers. It is very large (23ha) and open and birds can move away from disturbance to quieter areas without leaving the lake. The coarse angling season overlaps the months when wintering wildfowl are present and bankside disturbance by anglers, plus the competitive effects on food from the stocked fish (Chapter 2), drastically reduce the use of the most popular fishery lakes except by a few great crested grebes, mute swans and tufted ducks. Sailing and windsurfing take place on two lakes but as use is relatively slight in winter, the effect of these sports is not great.

It is self-evident that shooting causes disturbance to the intended quarry flocks. However, as with other activities, the birds can tolerate well-managed shooting pressure if they have alternative feeding and roosting areas to choose from. Most inland wildfowling makes up a small part of a day in which pheasants are the principal quarry. An early morning attempt on the ducks will sometimes begin a day, or the 'evening flight' will be the final stand. Rearing and releasing ducks is not as widely practised as it is in the USA.

Two small shoots operate on the Great Linford site and neighbouring land. Five to ten days shooting per season result in a small bag of ducks and a few feral geese (the syndicates are actively encouraged to shoot the geese, see Chapter 5). Shooting leads to a temporary increase in ducks in the reserve, as it is recognised by them as a refuge, but no long-term effects have been discernible.

Where duck shooting is pursued, the benefits to wildfowl can outweigh the losses. Lakes are managed to encourage the birds, predators may be controlled and many wildfowlers are quick to cease shooting in hard weather and to provide supplementary food.

Requirements for roosting and feeding wildfowl

Roosting

Shelter is important to both feeding and sleeping birds. Some ducks, especially mallard and teal, prefer to rest on quiet sheltered banks with an open aspect, close to the water where they feel secure. The diving ducks sleep out in open water where no predator can approach without being seen. In windy weather these sleeping flocks will be in the lee of sheltering land vegetation such as scrub or trees.

Feeding

Water depth is a very important factor controlling the productivity of freshwater habitat. Water more than 2m deep is the least valuable feeding habitat for wildfowl. Many gravel pits are deeper than this but remedial measures which reduce depth at the margins can much increase their value to wildfowl. In deep water, light penetration is poor, leading to little or no plant growth and low temperatures. Diving ducks feeding on benthic invertebrates will use deeper areas but they must expend more energy to do so.

A long, convoluted shoreline with a very gentle gradient (1:15) maximises the warm productive shallows in a lake. The reserve lakes at Great Linford were designed with complex shore shapes and profiles to provide a diversity of micro-habitats to attract a range of wildfowl. Average depth in the lakes is 1.5m with a range of <0.5m to 4m.

Sheltered bays are often preferred feeding sites for dabbling ducks, though after windy weather stranded seeds and dislodged invertebrates can provide good feeding on an exposed shore.

Generally, flooded pits become more productive as they age. Colonisation of newly-flooded gravel pits by plants and animals is determined by the proximity of possible colonists and by the initial conditions, wave action, silt load, water depth and organic content of the sediments. At Great Linford the chain of lakes are in the floodplain of the River Great Ouse and, on average, are inundated by the river once a year. Plants, invertebrates and fish can therefore easily colonise the waters.

In the Great Linford reserve the lakes are now over 20 years old. As a result of the initial design and subsequent management, the feeding requirements of a wide range of wildfowl are satisfied. There is abundant undisturbed grazing available to geese, wigeon and coots; there are marshy areas and invertebrate-rich shallows for dabbling ducks. Herbivorous diving ducks and coots exploit the submerged weed beds and others forage for benthic invertebrates. Plentiful small fish are present and exploited by piscivorous species such as great crested grebes, goldeneye and goosander.

Wildfowl at Great Linford

In total 36 species of swans, geese and ducks have been recorded in the reserve at Great Linford (Table 4.1). In winter there is a large mixed flock of non-migratory feral Canada and greylag geese on the site. Other geese are seen with these birds occasionally and most are regarded as escaped captive-bred birds unless their appearance and behaviour strongly suggest that they are wild. Black swan and some ducks are also undoubtedly 'escapes'. Numbers of mute swans in the reserve are often highest in August but they remain numerous well into winter, leaving as the submerged weed beds diminish. Migratory swans are seen almost annually on passage in autumn and spring, but they rarely stay more than a day. Bewick's swan is more numerous than whooper swan, maximum numbers being 24 and 8 respectively.

The reserve lakes in winter attract a wide range of species of duck. Shelduck, pintail, goldeneye, smew

Table 4.1 Species of wildfowl recorded in the reserve at Great Lindord 1972-1992. * wild status in doubt

Canada goose	Gadwall
*Barnacle goose	Wigeon
Brent goose	Pintail
Greylag goose	*White-cheeked pintail
White-fronted goose	Garganey
*Bean goose	Shoveler
Pink-footed goose	*Red crested pochard
*Snow goose	Pochard
*Bar-headed goose	Tufted duck
Mute swan	Scaup
Whooper swan	Eider
Bewick's swan	Common scoter
*Black swan	Velvet scoter
*Ruddy shelduck	Goldeneye
Shelduck	Smew
*Egyptian goose	Goosander
Mallard	Ruddy duck
Teal	Mandarin duck

and goosander occur annually in small numbers. Smew and goosander are seen in larger numbers and remain longer when severe weather occurs in northern Europe. The four species of sea duck on the British list, scaup, eider, velvet scoter and common scoter have each been recorded only once, usually after stormy weather. North American ruddy duck have regularly been recorded in small numbers since the mid-1980s, as the feral British population has expanded. There are also occasional sightings of feral mandarin ducks. Garganey are transitory visitors with one or two being recorded annually, mostly in spring. Seven species of duck are regular winter visitors to the reserve in considerable numbers. Changes in their populations and distribution on the site are discussed below.

Monitoring wildfowl at Great Linford in winter

Winter wildfowl counts have been carried out at Great Linford by Game Conservancy staff since 1972. These fortnightly counts take place from September to March and include all fifteen water bodies on the site. Changes in lake use by wildfowl in winter (excluding feral geese) were analysed by Phillips (1992) using data for ten seasons, 1974/75 to 1978/79 and 1984/85 to 1988/89. The mean of the three highest counts (of total wildfowl or individual species) in each season was used to give an estimate of the regular population present. This figure is a standard parameter developed by the Wildfowl and Wetlands Trust (Owen, Atkinson-Willes & Salmon, 1986). The analysis revealed that the species content has changed from predominantly dabbling ducks in the earlier period, when most lakes were newly flooded, to greater numbers of submerged macrophyte feeders (eg. coot, mute swan and gadwall) in the later period. Diving duck numbers were little changed.

The highest count of wildfowl on the Linford site during the two study periods was 2216 birds in November 1988. Total numbers of ducks using the site in the two periods were similar but numbers of some common species changed markedly (Table 4.2).

On average, mallard comprised 41% of the wildfowl population in the early period but only 18% in the later period, numbers having almost halved. Coot numbers had, by contrast, substantially increased to make it the most common species, comprising 35% of the birds seen. Mute swan and gadwall were also significantly commoner in the later period. Like coot they feed on submerged macrophytes. Another herbivorous species, wigeon, also increased significantly.

The replacement of dabbling ducks, which were most numerous in the 70s, by those herbivorous species which are largely dependent on submerged macrophytes is evidence of a succession which has been observed elsewhere. Milne (1974) studied a new gravel pit for 10 years and recorded an increase in

Table 4.2 Regular (and maximum) counts of common ducks and of mute sean and coot in two 5-season periods, 1974/75-78/79 and 1984/85-88/89, at Great Linford. (Significance being indicated as follows: n.s. - not significant, * - P < 0.05, ** - P < 0.01.)

Species	1974-79	1984-89	Site Trend (Z test)	National Trend
Mute Swan *Cygnus olor*	23 (50)	57 (132)	increase*	Stable (increase on gravel pits
Wigeon *Anas penelope*	157 (401)	335 (747)	increase**	stable
Gadwall *Anas strepera*	2.2 (8)	10 (27)	increase	increase**
Teal *Anas crecca*	137 (323)	87 (183)	n.s.	stable
Mallard *Anas platyrhynchos*	529 (1202)	264 (457)	decrease**	stable
Pochard *Aythya ferina*	123 (384)	136 (242)	n.s.	decrease
Tufted Duck *Aythya fuligula*	229 (435)	179 (341)	n.s.	stable
Coot *Fulica atra*	265 (446)	516 (767)	increase**	stable

National Trends from IWRB Special Publication No.8.

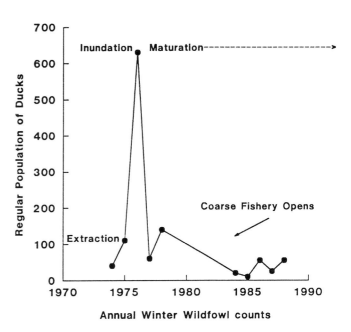

dabbling ducks in the early stages, followed by the establishment of diving duck flocks in the maturing pit as the dabbling duck populations dwindled. In the mid-1970s most water bodies at Great Linford were newly created or still partially in work. They therefore had changing shorelines. Newly inundated, partially-vegetated land resulted in temporarily productive, shallow feeding areas for dabbling ducks, especially

Figure 4.2 After extraction of minerals finished on Dovecote Lake and the workings flooded, there was a six-fold increase in the number of ducks, especially mallard and teal. This effect lasted only one season. We believe that the subsequent stocking of the lake for a coarse fishery led to a suppression of the food available for waterfowl and hence the continued low usage to the present day by ducks.

Wintering wildfowl on Main Lake.

Ducks feeding on weeds.

Mute swan: their numbers have increased as vegetation has colonised the lake beds.

mallard. Such effects are short-lived, as was shown at Dovecote Lake. This lake has the best recorded history of any lake on the site.

In 1976/77, wildfowl numbers at Dovecote increased six-fold (Figure 4.2). This was the first season after full inundation of the lake, following completion of gravel extraction. Large areas of reinstated land which had been recolonised by plants were flooded for the first time. The increase in total wildfowl numbers was largely due to a great increase in dabbling ducks; 50% of the birds present were mallard and 19% were teal. The effect lasted only one season, followed by a sharp decline in numbers in the next. Relatively few wildfowl were counted at Dovecote between 1984 and 1989. By this time the lake had become an important angling water and was heavily stocked with coarse fish, especially bream and roach. The impact of a high density of fish on waterfowl feeding conditions may have

suppressed any potential increase in wildfowl numbers during maturation. Competition for food between fish and ducks has been a major line of investigation in the study of the ecology of gravel pits at Great Linford.

Changes in winter wildfowl numbers following the removal of fish

Improvements in wildfowl breeding success after the fish populations of the reserve lakes were removed (Chapter 2) have been accompanied by marked increases in use by wildfowl in winter.

Table 4.3 shows a comparison of the use of two adjacent, similar lakes by wildfowl before and after the removal of fish from one. Both lakes had a high density of coarse fish until November 1987 when fish were removed from Main Lake. Blackhorse Lake is outside the reserve and was chosen for comparison because the two lakes were once contiguous and they have similarities of depth and benthic environment (both were wet-dug). Wildfowl numbers at Blackhorse Lake changed little during the period. In the reserve, the most immediate changes following fish removal were substantial increases in numbers of the herbivorous species: coot, mute swan and gadwall. Large numbers of coots and mute swans were noted feeding on Main Lake for the first time in the first autumn after fish removal. Numbers of shoveler also increased significantly in the post-removal period. Pochard showed no change in total numbers on site but a significant increase on Main Lake. There was a significant upward trend in tufted duck numbers on the whole site during this period but the increase in birds on Main Lake following fish removal was not significant.

No clear trend in changes in numbers of the two commonest dabbling ducks, mallard and teal, could be found; estimates of regular winter populations fluctuated widely. A considerable proportion of mallard and teal at Great Linford were on Main Lake in both periods.

The increased attractiveness of Main Lake without fish compared to the other lakes in the Great Linford complex is shown in Table 4.4.

Table 4.4 The percentage of the total population of each species at the Great Linford site present at Main Lake in pre- and post- fish removal seasons.

	% of site population	
Species	pre-removal 1984-87	post-removal 1988-91
Mute Swan	9.3	55.4
Wigeon	46.3	34.5
Gadwall	26.0	55.2
Teal	65.5	69.3
Mallard	60.1	53.7
Shoveler	43.8	85.8
Pochard	30.7	61.2
Tufted Duck	21.8	24.5
Coot	0.5	36.9
Mean	20.5	40.2

Table 4.3 Mean regular populations of common ducks, mute swan and coot in pre- and post- fish removal seasons at the Main Lake(ML) and Blackhorse Lake(BL). Trends for the whole Great Linford site are included for comparison. Statistical significance levels are n.s. = not significant, * = p < .05, ** = p < .01, *** = p,.001.

		Mean of 3 highest counts/season			
Species		pre-removal 1984-87	post-removal	Difference (z test)	Site Trend
Mute Swan	ML	3.6	69.3	**	increase
	BL	1.5	2.0	n.s.	**
Wigeon	ML	181.7	124.9	n.s.	no trend
	BL	18.0	0	n.s.	
Gadwall	ML	1.1	19.6	***	increase
	BL	0	0		**
Teal	ML	55.1	50.1	n.s.	no trend
	BL	0	0		
Mallard	ML	196.1	159.1	n.s	no trend
	BL	4.7	3.0	n.s	
Shoveler	ML	4.3	36.3	**	increase
	BL	2.2	1.3	n.s.	**
Pochard	ML	40.0	82.2	*	no trend
	BL	6.1	7.2	n.s.	
Tufted Duck	ML	39.7	55	n.s	increase
	BL	12.9	25.3	n.s.	*
Coot	ML	2.1	203.1	***	no trend
	BL	3.8	3.7	n.s.	

Main Lake held more than 50% of the regular winter populations of six of the nine common species in the first three years after fish removal. Its percentage share of total wildfowl counted (excluding geese) has doubled and continues to rise. In December 1991, 2200 wildfowl (excluding feral geese) were counted at Great Linford, close to the site record of 2216. 56% of these birds were in the reserve area.

The status of common wildfowl at Great Linford

Mute Swan

Mute swan breeding pairs are usually highly territorial but most join the non-breeding birds in flocks from August onwards. Submerged aquatic plants provide the bulk of their diet. They also eat some emergent vegetation and will graze grasses and some cereals.

In any one year, from one to seven pairs of swans have bred at Great Linford and flocks have been present regularly on the southern Trout Lake and Haversham Lake in winter. Feeding swans were rarely seen on the reserve Main Lake until the fish were removed in late 1987. In the first autumn following the fish removal, swan numbers soared; 163 birds were present in October. The new extensive submerged weed beds of *Elodea canadensis* (Canadian pondweed) and *Potamogeton pectinatus* (fennel-leaved pondweed), continue to attract these birds (Figure 4.3). The greatest numbers coincide with the end of the breeding season and the peak time for weed growth (August) but some

stay feeding on the lake until late winter. An adult swan eats about 4kg of water plants per day, so a flock of 125 birds can remove half a tonne of aquatic vegetation per day. The submerged weed beds of Main Lake have supported this considerable impact by the swans for four successive autumn/winter seasons.

Mallard

Mallard breed in the reserve at Great Linford and much of the research effort has been directed at identifying and implementing ways of increasing their numbers. The resident population is augmented in winter by considerable numbers of immigrants from further north.

Mallard are omnivorous but vegetable matter is more important than invertebrates in their winter diet. When feeding in the reserve they concentrate in the shallows and damp edges, probably taking seeds of docks (*Rumex* spp.), rushes (especially *Eleocharis* spp.) and persicarias (*Polygonum* spp). Early research into Mallard diet by Street (1975) found that surrounding agricultural land was the principal feeding area in autumn and winter. Grain formed a high proportion of the diet. At that time it was readily available, as stubble was routinely left until spring. Farming practice has changed to mainly winter crops, so little stubble is left for ducks to feed on. They do still feed out of the reserve in wet field flashes and ditches but more are seen feeding in the lake margins. Overall numbers have not changed significantly since the fish were removed. As the lakes have always provided attractive loafing and roosting areas this may disguise changes in feeding use.

Teal

The diet and feeding behaviour of teal are similar to those of mallard but competition between the species is avoided as teal specialise in smaller items. Waterplant and ruderal (annual plant) seeds are very important to teal and chironomid larvae and snails are taken when abundant. Teal are more wary than mallard and accurate counting is made difficult by their preference for marshy ground with considerable cover. At Great Linford this species once preferred the smaller, less open Stanton Low lake to the larger Main Lake. However, when the Main Lake bund was created in 1989 teal were attracted to its wet flashes. A dense annual flora develops each year on the bund consisting of docks (*Rumex* spp.), fat hen and other goosefoots (*Chenopodium* spp.), persicarias (*Polygonum* spp.) and grasses. Winter flooding submerges much of this growth and creates perfect conditions for feeding teal. Between 80 and 100 birds were counted on the bund

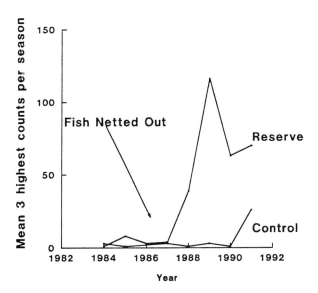

Figure 4.3 Wintering mute swan numbers (mean of the three highest counts per season) on the Linford reserve Main Lake and an adjacent control (Black Horse Lake) where no fish removal has occurred. Note the sharp increase in swan numbers after the fish removal from the reserve.

Teal in *Phragmites*: wary and hard to count.

in January 1992. Regular winter populations of teal have not increased significantly since fish removal from the lakes.

Gadwall

The reserve lakes at Great Linford have recently become an important site for gadwall in winter. The Joint Nature Conservation Committee considers a site of national importance if it regularly supports at least 1% of the national total of a species. Regular numbers are determined using the average of the previous five year's peak counts. Gadwall numbers nationally have

been increasing in Britain in winter for some time. They have become much more common at Great Linford, where only one or two per winter were seen in the 1970s. The increase in their numbers in the reserve following the removal of the fish has, however, been dramatic (Figure 4.4). Up to 78 have been counted and there are regularly more than 50 present (1% of the national winter population). Fox & Mitchell (1988) described the origins of the gadwall in Britain in winter. Ringing recoveries showed that 33-50% of the birds were from eastern Europe.

The increasing gadwall population has taken advantage of the increased availability of gravel pits and reservoirs. This species is herbivorous, concentrating on submerged vegetation. They can feed by dabbling and up-ending in shallow water but Fox (1991) largely attributes their success to another feeding behaviour. Gadwall can utilise submerged weeds growing in deep water by practising kleptoparasitism on coots which dive for their food. Coots are messy eaters often bringing more weed to the surface than they consume. Feeding mute swans too can provide food for gadwall in this way. No other species has adopted this energetically sound behaviour and therefore their expansion has taken place without competition. Once the extensive weed beds established in Main Lake,

Shoveler flock feeding by the near hide on Main Lake.

Drake pochard.

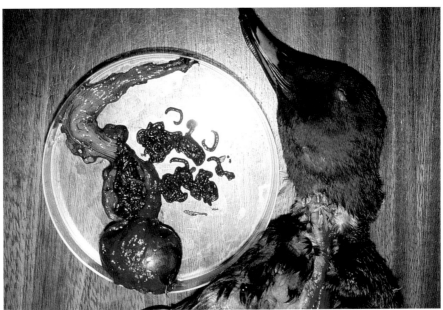

Pochard autopsy:
a diet of midge larvae.

large flocks of coots and mute swans gathered in the reserve. These have attracted increasing numbers of gadwall which feed almost exclusively by stealing weed at the surface from the other species.

Shoveler

Shoveler were scarce at Great Linford in the mid-1970s but there was a substantial increase in the population in the 1980s. In the period 1984/85 to 1986/87 the average peak count was 9.9 birds compared to an average peak count of 42 birds in 1988/89 and 1990/91. Much of the increase was attributable to higher counts in the reserve (Figure 4.5) where the average regular count from 1988/89 to 1990/91 was 36.3 birds. Shoveler eat more animal matter than other dabbling ducks. The food is strained from the water with fine bill lamellae which

act as a filter-feeding structure. This species has probably benefited from the increased abundance of tiny snails, crustacea (eg *Daphnia magna*) and insect larvae in the reserve lakes since the fish were removed. The increased population of shoveler is especially welcome as the species is thought to be in decline in northwest Europe.

Pochard

Immigrant pochard arrive in Britain from the Baltic and the USSR. Numbers rose to a peak in the 1970s, apparently in response to the increased available habitat as more gravel pits and reservoirs were flooded. However, the species may now be in a decline. At Great Linford there was little change in the size of the winter population between the mid 1970s and 1980s. The species prefers relatively

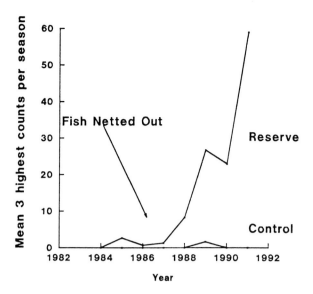

Figure 4.4 Wintering gadwall numbers (mean of the three highest counts per season) on the Linford reserve Main Lake and an adjacent control (Black Horse Lake) where no fish removal has occurred. Note the sharp increase in gadwall numbers after the fish removal from the reserve.

large areas of open water for both roosting and feeding. Their distribution at Great Linford reflected this preference, though large waters with high fish populations (and therefore, bankside disturbance and less food) were avoided. Haversham and the southern Trout Lake were the most used.

Pochard are omnivorous, taking a range of plant and animal food chiefly by diving. Animal prey, mainly chironomid larvae, become increasingly important as

winter progresses and submerged plants die back. Three out of a sample of nine pochard shot on the southern Trout Lake in December 1989 contained food in the upper digestive tract. Two contained solely large chironomid larvae; the other had fed on *Eristalis* larvae (rat-tailed maggots) which are found in rich farm ponds and ditches.

Following the removal of fish from the reserve lakes, more pochard were seen feeding on Main Lake and a study of their behaviour there and at the southern Trout Lake was undertaken (Phillips, 1991). Feeding at both sites was restricted to relatively small areas of the shallow water zone (0.9-1.6m average depth). Chironomid larvae were present in significantly higher numbers in feeding areas than at similar depths elsewhere. The birds were sensitive to relatively small differences in habitat quality, detecting as little as 17% difference in prey density. In gravel pit lakes, where productivity builds up gradually, this ability to find the highest concentration of food could be of high survival value.

Figure 4.6 shows the regular populations of pochard in the reserve and the changes since fish were removed from the lakes. The birds appeared to respond quickly to the increased food available in the absence of fish. However the peak numbers of 1989/90 have not been recorded since. The recent creation of the dividing bund across the lake has effectively created two smaller lakes. Fox (1991) noted that pochard tend to avoid lakes below 6ha in area and they may now perceive the reserve lakes as too enclosed.

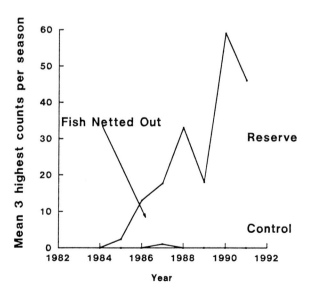

Figure 4.5 Wintering shoveler numbers (mean of the three highest counts per season) on the Linford reserve Main Lake and an adjacent control (Black Horse Lake) where no fish removal has occurred. Note the sharp increase in shoveler numbers after the fish removal from the reserve.

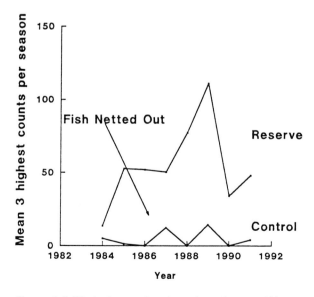

Figure 4.6 Wintering pochard numbers (mean of the three highest counts per season) on the Linford reserve Main Lake and an adjacent control (Black Horse Lake) where no fish removal has occurred. Note the increase in pochard numbers after the fish removal from the reserve.

Wigeon

In winter, wigeon feed in tight flocks. They take seeds and other plant material from the water surface, and may feed amongst other open water species such as tufted duck and pochard, or they graze short herbage on lake shores and marshy areas. They are usually extremely wary and as they are often on the shore they are susceptible to disturbance.

Wigeon numbers increased significantly at Great Linford between the 1970s and 1980s. In the later period, gravel extraction had ceased and the lakes were separated by large areas of rough sheep grazing where there was very little human disturbance. Removal of fish from the reserve lakes has not had a significant effect on wigeon numbers but there have been interesting changes in their feeding behaviour. Wigeon begin to arrive in autumn in late August or September. Before the fish removal, wigeon were observed throughout the season grazing on the lake shores. Once submerged weed beds established in the absence of fish, wigeon began to feed on Main Lake itself. In 1989 and 1990 this behaviour was observed in September and October, when the birds reverted to shore grazing. In 1991 they were still surface feeding in late December before switching at the end of the year.

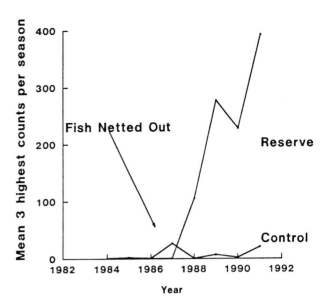

Figure 4.8 Wintering coot numbers (mean of the three highest counts per season) on the Linford reserve Main Lake and an adjacent control (Black Horse Lake) where no fish removal has occurred. Note the sharp increase in coot numbers after the fish removal from the reserve.

Tufted Duck

Tufted duck breed in the reserve in small numbers but more broods have been observed since the removal of fish (Chapter 2). An increase in availability of their principal food, gastropod molluscs, has been suggested as the cause of increased use of the reserve by both breeding and wintering tufted ducks (see Figure 4.7). Giles (1990) demonstrated experimentally the ability of tufted ducks to increase their success rate in capturing food in each dive in direct proportion to the amount of food available. The increased food available in the lake would therefore make it a more profitable feeding area. Roosting flocks also utilise the sheltered open water.

Coot

Coots are a common and familiar species of inland waters. They are principally herbivorous, although they have a reputation as egg predators. In general coots feed either by diving for submerged weeds or they graze. They often congregate in large numbers and they have been quick to exploit man-made habitats such as gravel pits. Numbers at Great Linford increased significantly between the 1970s and 1980s. However, it was not until the first autumn after the fish were removed from the reserve lakes that coot began to feed on Main Lake. The extensive beds of *Elodea* and *Potamogeton* have been heavily exploited by this species ever since. Numbers decline later in the winter as remaining weeds die-back. Figure 4.8 shows the dramatic increase in coots in the reserve.

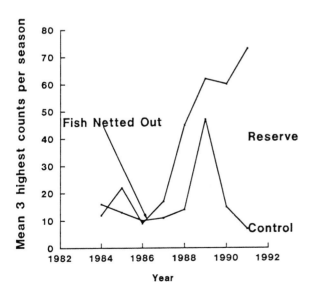

Figure 4.7 Wintering tufted duck numbers (mean of the three highest counts per season) on the Linford reserve Main Lake and an adjacent control (Black Horse Lake) where no fish removal has occurred. Tufted duck numbers have risen in the reserve since the fish removal. The adjacent control lake also showed a short-term increase but this has now declined, whilst the reserve numbers are still rising.

The importance of Great Linford to wildfowl in the winter months

Increasing numbers of ducks and geese are spending the winter within the Great Linford site. They are responding to a variety of factors. The lakes are aging and becoming ecologically more mature, providing better feeding conditions and more marginal cover for those species that require it. The site is relatively undisturbed by human activity and is large enough for birds to move within it as conditions dictate. The reserve itself forms the core area, offering increasingly rewarding feeding conditions and safety, but this is only part of the chain of good habitat that is available. The reserve lakes are of county importance for their wildfowl populations and the current high use by gadwall is of national significance.

Winter wildfowl and fisheries

Research has clearly shown that high fish populations damage wildfowl feeding habitat and stocked angling lakes have low wildfowl populations as a result. It has also shown that immigrant wildfowl respond rapidly to changes in weed growth and increased invertebrate food supply which result from fish removal. Lakes can, therefore, be "aged" in this way to enhance them as habitat for wildfowl in winter.

The slow process of vegetation growth in flooded gravel pit lakes, where extraction has ended, may be speeded up by suppression of the fish populations in the early stages. Similarly, wildfowl on older lakes with high fish populations are likely to benefit if the larger fish are netted out at intervals (leaving immature fish to grow on and to provide food for piscivorous waterfowl).

Gravel extraction has created new habitat for wintering wildfowl and boosted the UK population of several important species of duck.

CHAPTER 5

MANAGEMENT OF FERAL GEESE ON GRAVEL PITS

The Introduction of Canada geese

Canada geese originate from North America, where the species breeds over a very large area, from the central USA northwards to Alaska and West Greenland. There is considerable variation in size and colouration within the species, from the tiny Western Alaskan race *Branta canadensis minima*, also called the cackling goose, which at 1.5 to 2kg is not much bigger than a mallard duck, to the giant Canada goose *B.c.maxima* from the south of the range, which weighs up to 9kg. The larger races are usually sedentary, while the smaller races undertake long annual migrations between their far-northern nesting grounds and wintering areas in the southern states.

Canada geese were originally introduced into Britain in the 1660s, for their ornamental value as well as to provide sport in areas of the country where there were no breeding greylag geese (see Giles 1990). It is usually assumed that the subspecies introduced into Europe was *B.c.canadensis*, from the central States and the southern part of the Atlantic breeding range, although recently it has been suggested that at least some British birds are large enough to be giant Canadas (Owen 1977).

Canada and greylag geese have multiplied rapidly on gravel pits and this has caused many problems.

Canada geese were first introduced at St James' Park, London, and were subsequently released on many private estates in southern England, where they were protected from unrestricted shooting. With little standing water in southern Britain until recent decades, the small isolated populations of sedentary geese were initially slow to spread of their own accord, and the British breeding range hardly expanded for three centuries. More recently, as numbers continued to increase in areas where they had been introduced, the then Wildfowl Trust and Wildfowlers Association of Great Britain and Ireland (now the Wildfowl and Wetlands Trust and the British Association for Shooting and Conservation respectively) established new colonies in suitable breeding areas by translocating surplus eggs, and geese caught while moulting and flightless. In this way the geese were introduced throughout England and into a few areas of Scotland, Wales and Northern Ireland. Since the passing of the Wildlife and Countryside Act of 1981, it is now illegal to introduce these geese. However, they are continuing to spread unaided and have colonised urban and suburban ponds and lakes and especially flooded mineral workings along the valleys of rivers such as the Great Ouse, Thames, Nene and Trent.

Restored sand and gravel workings provide very suitable breeding and roosting habitats for Canada and greylag geese alike, with islands for nesting and often grassland for feeding. In 1970 it was estimated that each year the aggregates industry was creating about 1000 hectares of open water through the flooding of disused workings. Over much of lowland Britain, therefore, the density of artificial water bodies is such that there is no barrier to the spread of even the most sedentary of birds.

Many British Canada geese have remained completely sedentary, never flying more than a few kilometres from their birthplace. However, some undertake quite long migrations to and from moulting areas at the end of the summer. For example many Yorkshire birds congregate at the Beauly Firth, Inverness-shire, in summer (Walker 1970). This parallels their behaviour in their native range. Many birds which nest in Sweden and Finland migrate to Denmark and the Low Countries to spend the winter (Madsen & Andersson 1990).

With safe nesting, abundant food and few predators, the British Canada goose population has increased very rapidly. The first attempt to assess the numbers in Britain was made in 1953, when between 2000 and 4000 birds were estimated to be present (Owen 1977). During the next few years numbers increased rapidly as more were transported away from areas where the geese were becoming an agricultural pest and into new

sites. Numbers have continued to increase, at a national average rate of 8.5% per year between 1964 and 1989, giving an estimated total population in Britain of about 51 000 in 1988, a figure projected possibly to rise to 135 000 by the year 2000. There has been considerable variation in the rate of increase across the country (Salmon 1991; Table 5.1).

Table 5.1 The annual growth rates since 1976 for various groups of Canada geese as defined by Ogilvie (1977).

Area	Annual growth rate %
Cumbria	13.4
Yorkshire	5.5
Derbyshire	3.8
Nottinghamshire	8.8
Shropshire/Cheshire	7.5
Anglesey	NS
West Midlands	9.0
Norfolk	NS
Thames Basin	13.9

NS = No significant change

In Anglesey and Norfolk no significant increase has been recorded. Little new man-made habitat has become available in these areas, and comparatively intense shooting has probably helped to keep the numbers here fairly stable. Similarly, in north-east England and Scotland the geese are probably controlled by shooting and little new habitat has become available. Here the increase has been only 1.9% per annum. The central England and north Wales areas have had an increase of 7.3% and south-west England and south Wales 10.4%. The greatest increase has taken place in south-east England with 12.3% per year overall. Here the rise in the population in the Thames Valley has been a major contributor to the regional increase; there were 5000 geese here by 1976; there may well have been 20 000 in 1991.

The increase has been much greater in favourable habitats, notably 19.5% per year at gravel pits and 20% per year on reservoirs. The great increase in these habitats has been due partly to an increase in density at existing sites, and partly to the continuing creation of new habitat as mineral workings are flooded. The provision of nesting islands in flooded workings in an attempt to improve them for wildlife has been a significant factor in the expansion of the population. On older lakes in contrast, many of which had already attained their carrying capacity in the 1960s, the increase has been much less; 4.8% per year (Salmon 1991).

There is no sign yet that the rapid rate of population growth is starting to slow down. The breeding range in Britain, formerly patchy around points where geese were released into the wild, has consolidated and in-filled. It was completely unexpected in the 1970s that the Canada goose population would be as large as it is now (Ogilvie 1977).

Canada geese in the wild in North America feed in flocks on grass seeds on the prairies and natural wet-land vegetation such as wigeon grass, eel grass, bul-rush, sedges and the roots of spike rush. In Britain the adult geese eat grass, oilseed rape, cereal crops and root crops such as sugar beet, potatoes and turnips.

Great Linford is in many ways a typical south-east England site. Canada geese arrived here of their own accord in 1972. There were thirty nesting pairs by 1980, 45 in 1986 and over 100 by 1990. The winter flock has peaked at about 500 birds in recent years.

Greylag geese

The greylag goose breeds in Iceland, Britain and from Scandinavia and Eastern Europe eastwards to central Asia (Owen 1977). It is the only species of goose native to the British Isles. At one time it was probably fairly widespread here, but habitat destruction and hunting have steadily reduced the breeding range over the last few centuries. A population survived in the East Anglian fens until they were drained, compara-tively recently. These days the much-reduced remnant wild population is confined to parts of north and west Scotland and S W Scotland.

During the 1930s, greylags were reintroduced into south-west Scotland and East Anglia, and in the 1960s

and 1970s there was a more widespread introduction programme by the then Wildfowlers Association of Great Britain and Ireland (WAGBI). Reintroductions had the aim of re-establishing the species in England, primarily as a hunting quarry. WAGBI released more than 1300 geese, some taken directly from the wild Scottish population and some reared on the Associa-tion's reserves, and by the mid-1980s there were flocks at more than thirty sites (Owen & Salmon 1989).

Outside Scotland, flocks increased at a rate of about 13% per year, resulting in a population increase from about 1 700 birds at the end of the 1960s to around 14 000 by the mid-1980s. Most of this dramatic population growth has taken place in south-east Eng-land, particularly where artificial nesting and roosting habitat in the form of flooded mineral workings has become available. If the population were to continue to increase at this rate, there would be an estimated 96,000 greylags by the year 2000. However, available habitat, control by farmers, wildfowling, and competi-tion with Canada geese, will eventually put a ceiling on numbers.

Like Canada geese in Britain, feral greylags tend to be very sedentary, not travelling more than a few kilometres between their nesting, roosting and feeding areas.

Greylags are the most adaptable of European geese and these days almost all adult European greylags feed on agricultural land: on stubble and potato waste in autumn and early winter, changing to grass and sprouting cereals in late winter and spring. They will also eat turnips, kale, beans, carrots and newly-sown grain.

At the Great Linford ARC Wildfowl Centre, greylags were deliberately introduced in 1972, when sixteen birds were brought from Wigtownshire (now Dumfries and Galloway). Here as elsewhere they have increased in numbers dramatically, although there was a tem-porary check in the early 1980s. By 1991 there were about 50 breeding pairs, with a winter flock peaking at around the same level as the local Canada goose flock – about 500 birds.

Breeding biology of feral geese

Canada geese nest from late March onwards, greylags from early April. Canada geese lay usually five or six eggs per nest and greylags four to six. Nesting is mostly in colonies and often on islands. Where the two species occur together, as at the Great Lin-ford site, there is no tendency to form single-species colonies; nests of the two are completely intermingled.

Table 5.2 Sites and fates of Greylag and Canada Goose nests at Great Linford, combined data 1982-1986.

	Total		Destroyed by predators		Deserted	Flooded	Not hatched	Hatched
	I	M	I	M				
Greylag	119	12	16	9	11	2	2	91
Canada	132	14	15	10	7	1	1	101

I = Island nest site   M = Mainland nest site

However greylags tend to choose less open, more sheltered nest sites than Canadas.

The island nesting habit has evolved as an anti-predator measure, and colonial nesting for communal defence. Wright & Giles (1988) found that only 10% of Canada goose nests and only 9% of greylag nests at Great Linford were on the mainland (Table 5.2). This study revealed that mainland nests of both species suffered heavy mortality from predators, with 10 out of 14 mainland Canada nests and nine out of 12 mainland greylagg nests being lost. On islands only 13% of greylag nests and 11% of Canada nests suffered predation (Table 5.2).

The main predators are foxes, with crows and mink also being important in some areas. Foxes destroy goose nests and may remove eggs to a cache nearby. They are often disinclined to cross water, which explains the much lower predation rates on islands. When islands become accessible as water levels drop during dry weather, foxes are able to gain access to the islands, resulting sometimes in heavy predation. For example at Great Linford in 1984 on one island which became accessible, foxes took ten out of eleven goose nests. On other islands, where the water level remained high, only three out of 26 were predated, probably by crows (Wright & Giles 1988).

Disturbance by people may also be a factor lowering breeding success at some sites, by discouraging geese from making nests at all and/or by causing the birds to leave their eggs repeatedly uncovered during incubation. This does not often take place at Great Linford,

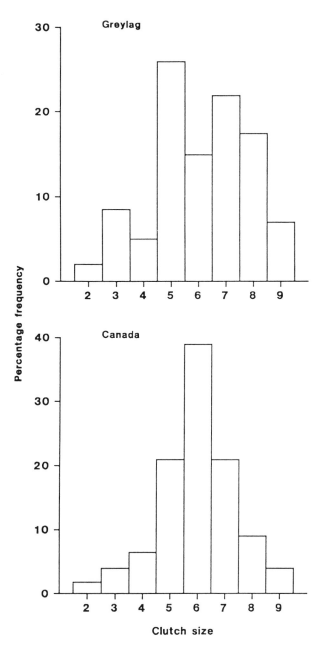

Figure 5.1 Percentage frequency distributions for greyleg and Canada goose clutch sizes.

Goose nest destroyed by a fox. Island nest sites are much less vulnerable to predators.

Canada geese guard their flightless, vulnerable brood

however, because there is no official public access to goose nesting areas.

In the same study of breeding biology, Wright & Giles found that of 79 greylag and 88 Canada nests successfully incubated to hatching at Great Linford. The average clutch size was 6.1 eggs per nest for both species. Clutch size ranged from two to nine eggs, with a more even spread of clutch sizes among greylags (Figure 5.1). There was no difference between the two species in the proportion of eggs which hatched, or in the proportion of nests which were destroyed by predators (Tables 5.2 and 5.3).

Greylags, however, raised more young to fledging per nest than Canadas: only 10% of greylags died but as many as 50% of Canada goslings died. This may be due to the earlier nesting of Canadas resulting in higher mortality during poor weather. Lessells (1986) found that the highest mortality rates among Canada goslings occurred soon after hatching and were associated with cold, wet conditions. On the other hand Fabricius (1983) found that in Sweden greylags suffer greater pre-fledging losses than Canada geese, possibly because greylag broods feed more on land and foxes are able to catch more goslings.

	Successful nests	Goslings hatched	Goslings fledged	Percentage mortality
1984				
Greylag	12	57	53	7
Canada	15	92	48	48
1985				
Greylag	21	93	82	12
Canada	25	138	60	56
1987				
Greylag	25	156	145	7
Canada	39	203	120	41

Table 5.3. Fledging success of Canada and greylag geese at at Great Linford in 1984, 1985 and 1987.

Overall, the breeding success of Canada geese at Great Linford is relatively low in comparison with some sites. In Manitoba for example a figure of 5.5 fledged goslings per nest was recorded by Klopman (1958) and Byrd & Woolington (1983) found a nest success of 90% and four fledglings per successful nest among Aleutian Canada geese (*B.c.leucopareia*) at Buldir Island, Alaska. Wright & Giles (1988) concluded that the overall low breeding success at Great Linford may be due to a high proportion of young, inexperienced birds in the relatively new and expanding population.

After hatching, the goslings remain flightless for eight to ten weeks and band together in creches which are guarded by one or more of the most dominant ganders in the breeding group. The geese attain sexual maturity and are capable of breeding at three to four years old.

Agricultural crop damage by feral geese

Because of their wide range of natural plant foods and their consequent readiness to take to feeding on a variety of crops, it was perhaps inevitable that feral geese would eventually come into conflict with agriculture. Conflicts had already begun to emerge in Britain by the early 1950s (Owen 1977). Canada geese have also come into conflict with farming in Scandinavia, where they were also introduced (Madsen & Andersson 1990) and in parts of their natural range in the United States (e.g. Craven *et al* 1985).

In Britain, the greatest potential for damage to crops arises during the spring, when the geese are feeding heavily to lay down fat to carry them though the energetically demanding nesting season. Total destruction of a crop can result from severe grazing pressure accompanied by trampling and heavy manuring at this time of the year (Owen 1991). Even less severe grazing in April and May can lead to a 50% reduction in spring barley yields.

Another potentially critical period comes in late summer and autumn, when flocks of geese, their numbers swollen by the year's production of young, can cause severe damage to unharvested crops.

As well as causing crop losses by direct consumption, geese paddle wet ground, crushing plants and compacting the soil so that a hard crust forms when the ground dries and the development of a healthy root system is inhibited. Large flocks of geese may cause significant damage in this way, especially in areas of heavier soils.

Although in a national context the amount of loss and damage to crops may be relatively insignificant, for individual farms and estates — especially those near watercourses and lakes — damage is often considerable. Yield losses of 20% have been recorded on winter cereal fields which were grazed by geese from germination until harvest time (Simpson 1991).

In spring, geese may spend up to 18 hours per day feeding on the new growing tips of spring grass, which is valued by farmers as a 'spring bite' for livestock. Grassland may be permanently damaged by geese — the grass becomes uprooted and the land overtaken by weeds. Re-seeding can be virtually impossible if there are many geese constantly on the land. On one East Midlands estate there was a suggestion that the rental values of grass keep were depressed by the presence of large numbers of Canada geese (Downing 1991).

The extent and seriousness of damage to crops varies considerably from place to place within Britain. The bulk of concern expressed by members of the Country Landowners' Association originates from the East Midlands (Downing 1991).

A survey carried out among 54 farms within a 10km radius of Great Linford Wildfowl Centre (Traill-

Stevenson 1987) revealed that only four of 30 farmers who responded had experienced problems with geese. Damage was very localised and always within 1km of the Great Linford roost. Grazing flocks ranged in size from only ten to about 250 birds, usually predominantly one or the other species. Roosting flocks ranged up to 800 birds, around 50% of each species. The geese came from the Great Linford site itself, from gravel pits at nearby Newport Pagnell, a country park at Emberton, from a wildlife conservation area at Stony Stratford and from lakes at Cosgrove and in Milton Keynes. These sites are all within 10km of Great Linford.

It appeared from this survey that the geese preferred some feeding sites over others. An ideal site, as well as providing a food source, is close to a large body of water for roosting and gives good views over the surrounding countryside so that the geese cannot be suddenly surprised by predators or people.

In this study the crops mostly affected were grass and winter barley, although comparatively few root crops are grown in this area so the apparent preference may be to some extent artificial. In 1988 a farmer in the Great Linford area first recorded damage to an oilseed rape crop. This crop, a 'double low' variety, was destroyed, and the field had to be completely resown with field beans at a cost of about £3000. 'Single low' varieties of rape which had been sown previously were apparently less palatable to geese and the almost complete change to 'double low' in recent years could be important in increasing the incidence of crop damage.

Other problems

While the main source of complaints, and the most economically significant, stems from the conflict between geese and agriculture, a number of other potentially important problems have emerged in recent years.

It is possible that Canada and greylag geese may compete with native wildfowl and other wildlife for nesting and roosting sites and for food. Little research has been carried out on this subject, but there are anecdotal reports of ducks and mute swans being driven away from their traditional sites by large numbers of geese, and there is a suggestion that in winter geese might compete with mute swans for grazing, for underwater food plants and for food provided by the public (Owen 1991).

At Great Linford, geese have been seen to flatten the vegetation around mallard nests, making them more vulnerable to predators. Canada geese have also been seen harassing breeding greylags, which, though feral and equally as likely to cause conflicts as Canadas, are arguably preferable since the species is at least indigenous to Britain. Such harassment may cause the greylags to abandon their nests.

Another increasingly prevalent source of complaints about feral geese results from the fouling of public amenity areas and other sites by goose droppings. Complaints arise naturally enough mostly in areas which are open to the public. The East Midlands Director of the National Trust (a major landowner in the region) has received many complaints from the public about fouling by geese (Downing 1991). Picnic areas may be rendered unusable and walking hazardous and unpleasant.

Geese are inefficient herbivores and are unable to digest cellulose. Canada geese for example are only able to absorb 25 to 30% of the food value contained in the vegetable material which they consume. This may be contrasted with a figure of 60% absorption achieved by sheep. Because of this, geese must consume large amounts of food, resulting in the production of correspondingly large amounts of manure. A single Canada goose produces about 875 grams of manure each day (corresponding to a dry weight of 175 grams per day). Not surprisingly, therefore, considerable fouling may result from large flocks of geese, especially in places where they habitually congregate, for example at public feeding points at lakesides. Considerable anxiety has been expressed about the potential heath hazard, especially to young children, and although there is no evidence that a health risk is involved, concern about the appearance and hygiene of areas frequented by geese is understandable. In 1991 the organisers of Henley Regatta were obliged to resort to fencing off part of the Thames in an attempt to prevent feral geese from 'turning the grass into a guano factory' and also from obstructing the racing (Daily Telegraph 30.5.91). One golf club leasing land from the National Trust, although it uses a Canada goose logo on its letterhead, is very concerned about the problem. Goose droppings adhere to shoes, golf clothes, caddy car wheels and even golf balls. The fairways are regularly brushed but the continuous labour required to keep the course clean has been compared to that required for painting the Forth Road Bridge (Downing 1991).

A final source of complaint is the perceived physical danger from geese. Ganders can be quite aggressive. Large flocks may be intimidating to those unfamiliar with them, and public fears have been expressed that accidents might occur, especially to small children. While there is no evidence that geese do constitute a

Grazing and fouling of public parks causes considerable problems.

danger, concern both among the public and among owners and managers of public sites is again understandable.

However, despite these problems and complaints, in many cases estate owners do not wish to see the geese completely eliminated. In spite of all their undesirable attributes, many people still find geese attractive and interesting and large numbers of people enjoy feeding them. They may therefore often be seen by owners and managers of amenity sites as a public attraction. Even so, owners wish to see goose flocks kept to reasonable and manageable numbers.

The shooting of geese has not been sufficient to stop their numbers escalating in the South of England.

Control measures

Given the established threat to agricultural crops, potential health and safety hazards and possible interference with other wildlife, it is not surprising that there have been calls for flocks of feral geese to be controlled in some way, either by removing the birds from the problem areas or by actually reducing their numbers. ARC and The Game Conservancy recognised the need for research into the feasibility of methods of controlling numbers of geese in 1987.

Many of the calls for control have been aimed specifically at Canada geese, but this is because they are more widespread and numerous and tend to be tamer than greylags. Feral greylag flocks can be equally troublesome. Because the two species' breeding biology and behaviour are similar, the same control methods may be applied to both species.

Feare (1991) listed and discussed a number of possible options for controlling geese as follows:

1. Taking no action;

2. Attempting to scare or discourage geese away from problem areas;

3. Increasing the presence of people so that the geese move away;

4. Altering the birds' habitat to make it unsuitable;

5. Increasing shooting in the open season;

6. Shooting in the close season, including shooting adults at or near the nest;

7. Narcotic chemicals;

8. Chemosterilisation;

9. Egg pricking or removal;

These options are discussed in turn below.

1. Taking no action

The rationale underlying the option of doing nothing is that eventually the numbers of geese will increase to the point where density-dependent 'natural' factors will cause populations to stabilise. One such effect might be the observed decrease in the breeding success of individual birds as colony size increases (Owen 1991). This option is attractive since it involves no labour or expense.

A major disadvantage, however, is that it may be very difficult, even impossible, to predict at what point any densitydependent effects would begin to operate, and what stable population levels would therefore have to be tolerated. In any case, this option is becoming more and more unattractive from a political or public relations point of view. Farmers and others who perceive geese as a problem will be increasingly unhappy if it appears that nothing is being done, and those responsible for managing the geese (ie landowners) will be increasingly reluctant to give the impression that they are doing nothing.

2. Scaring or discouraging geese

This may also appear to be an attractive option at first sight because it may be thought of as environmentally friendly and therefore likely to be acceptable to the public. Levels of expenditure and manpower required are also likely to be relatively low. Methods of scaring or discouragement include fencing to direct the birds to walk onto less valuable areas; scarers made for example from lengths of binder twine or plastic strip suspended over crops at intervals; various noisy 'bangers'; and scarecrows.

Perhaps the greatest disadvantage of this method is that feral geese very quickly become used to virtually any method of scaring which is tried. Scaring only works satisfactorily as a short-term measure, and it must only be used while geese are actually causing damage. Shooting in the open season can have the effect of making goose flocks more wary and easier to scare (Simpson 1991).

Another major drawback is that the geese are only scared away to another location. This may have the very undesirable effect of actually increasing the area over which crop damage or other problems are occurring. It is unknown whether scaring has any effect on overall numbers, but it would seem unlikely that the effect on long-term survival or breeding success would be very significant.

There is also the problem of the 'noise pollution' resulting from many banger-type scarers, especially in areas near to dwellings.

3. Increase disturbance

Increasing the level of casual human disturbance in areas frequented by geese, by encouraging public access, could have the same effect as deliberate scaring. The drawbacks are the same as with scaring: geese would probably quickly habituate to the presence of people or might be encouraged to spread. More importantly perhaps, a level of human disturbance sufficient to discourage geese would again be sure to disrupt other more desirable wildlife.

4. Habitat alterations

This would involve either managing breeding habitat to make it less suitable for geese, or altering agricultural cropping patterns to minimise the potential for damage. An advantage of this option would be that there is no need for legislation or licensing to carry out such changes. However there are disadvantages. Alteration of breeding habitat, as well as being potentially costly and labour intensive, might have deleterious effects on other, more desirable, birds and wildlife. For example the removal of nesting islands is likely to affect nesting by great crested grebes, ducks, terns and waders. Conservation and public relations considerations would therefore militate against this option. As for alteration of cropping patterns (for example by re-siting vulnerable crops further from the birds' roosting areas), it would seem very unlikely that this would ever be viewed by farmers as a widely applicable solution, since cropping regimes tend to be fairly rigid and are unlikely to be altered simply in response to a problem with geese.

5. Shooting in the open season

This might be seen as a very acceptable option by farmers since, if geese were controlled by sport shooting, the cost to farmers would be low and no legislative or licensing administration costs would be involved. It might be possible for farmers to derive income from the letting of inland wildfowling rights during the open season (1 September to 31 January).

Goose shooting is popular in Britain. It has been estimated that at least 13,000 people each year shoot wild geese for sport (Harradine 1991), although at present most goose shooting takes place in coastal areas (the main exception being in central Scotland).

Egg coll

7. Narcc

This is c
has bee
size of
the bird
has bee
any tim
be som
prove i
killed.

8. Chen

Render
wise da
cause a
be carr
narcoti
killing
accepte
areas \
present
siderab
before
chemic
tant to

It was concluded from these trials that even if the workforce is limited, so that it is not possible to remove eggs throughout the breeding season, it is still possible to limit the production of goslings significantly by replacing early clutches (those laid in the first two weeks of the season) with dummy eggs. As birds which start nesting later in the season do not lay replacement clutches, eggs from late pairs – usually considerably fewer in number – can be removed without the need for replacement.

Barnard (1991) used computer simulation modelling to assess the effectiveness of an egg-removal programme in reducing the numbers of Canada geese at Great Linford. Existing data were first used to calculate the size and age-structure of the Canada goose flock breeding there in early 1987. A population model was then developed based on the numbers of eggs produced by early and late nesters and re-layers, and known mortality rates. Comparison between the numbers predicted to be present in 1990 according to the model, and actual counts in the field in the same year, demonstrated that the model was accurate. It was therefore then used to estimate changes in the population size over the next decade, given varying levels of control.

It was calculated that if no egg collection at all were to take place, the flock would increase from c.300 birds in 1990 to c.2300 by the year 2000. The population could be held at a stable 1990 level by collecting 72% of eggs each year. If 95% of eggs were collected every year, numbers would fall to about 25% of the 1990 level by the year 2000 (Figures 5.5 and 5.6).

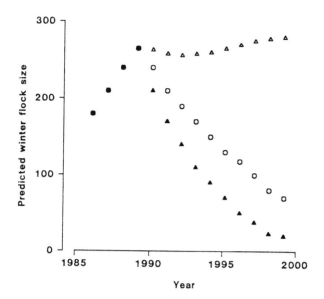

Figure 5.6 Output from a computer simulation model with predictions of the outcome of picking up 72% of eggs, 95% of eggs and 95% of eggs with 10% shooting pressure. Note how 72% egg-removal stabalizes the flock size whilst 95% egg-removal sends the population into rapid decline (with or without shooting).

It was estimated that it would take six years to halve the numbers of geese in a colony if all eggs were removed every year, given average annual adult mortality rates.

It is intended to extend the model to investigate the numbers of nests from which eggs must be removed in order to limit population growth or to cause a decrease.

MAFF have also experimented with a technique involving immersing eggs briefly in liquid paraffin, either at the beginning of incubation or after having been incubated for four days. Both laboratory and field trials have been carried out. No eggs which had been dipped in paraffin hatched, so this would appear to be a potentially very effective method of control. However, it seems likely that clearance under the Control of Pesticides Regulations would be required before the technique could be widely used.

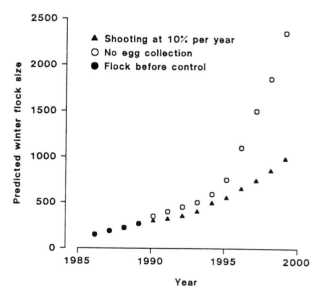

Figure 5.5 Output from a computer simulation model which predicts that the Linford Canada goose flock would reach 2,300 by the year 2000 with continued shooting and no egg collection.

Goose control: conclusions

Simpson (1991) concluded that it is necessary to utilise all possible methods for controlling the numbers of feral geese. Perhaps most importantly, for any programme to succeed it must have the full support of estate owners, farmers and managers of the waters frequented by geese. Ultimately the initiative to co-operate and coordinate action must come from those suffering damage.

Feare (1991) suggested that there needs to be a change in attitude by pest controllers, biologists and policy administrators. In order to reduce the national feral goose problems to a sustained low level, management and funding on a national level will be required to incorporate and coordinate the various schemes (shooting, scaring, egg pricking, etc.) which already take place at a local level. Most importantly, further research is needed into the biology and population dynamics of the geese in relation to the various methods of control.

The research at Great Linford into the effects of egg removal and substitution has proved that control by limiting the production of goslings is practicable.

Goose population control

At Great Linford, complaints from farmers regarding crop damage by geese led to research into humane methods of goose population control. This work will become increasingly important in future years as the goose population grows and expands into new habitats. The substitution of the freshly laid clutch with hard boiled eggs leads to geese incubating often for longer than the normal period and then giving up the annual breeding attempt to try again the following year. As goose nests on gravel pits are usually relatively easy to find, eggs are readily collected. Mainland nesting geese are usually isolated pairs and most of these nests are destroyed by foxes. A MAFF licence is required to pick up goose eggs during the breeding season and this will only be granted if significant damage to agricultural land by geese can be demonstrated by the landowner. This is, however, our recommended goose control policy.

Other potential control options include the following methods, each may be applicable at a given site depending upon local circumstances:

Shooting birds within the wildfowling season (September 1 – January 31).

Shooting breeding adults (under licence).

Culling adults during the moult period (mid-summer, also under licence).

Scaring with 'gas bangers' or other devices.

Changing the habitat to make it unattractive to the birds.

Narcotising adult birds (under licence).

A radio-tagged Canada goose with hatching goslings. Game Conservancy research at Great Linford has shown how the goose population explosion can be managed.

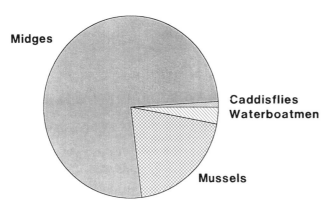

Figure 6.7 Pie chart showing composition of St Peters Lake bream diet in 1987.

Invertebrate food available for fish and waterfowl

Invertebrate samples from the two reserve study lakes for 1986 and 1987 produced the information shown in Tables 6.1 and 6.2 (see page 90).

Fish diet

In our 1986 studies, perch (Figures 6.1, 6.2) were found to eat non-biting midge (chironomidae) pupae, whereas bream (Figure 6.3) (in St Peter's Lake) ate mostly chironomid larvae and mussels. Tench in St Peter's (the species is rare in Main Lake) were more catholic in their tastes, eating a wide variety of aquatic

Figure 6.8 Pie chart showing composition of Main Lake bream diet in 1987.

Figure 6.9 Pie chart showing composition of St Peters Lake tench diet in 1987.

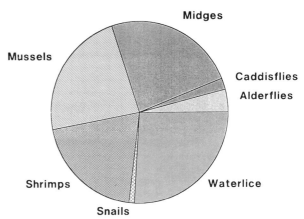

Perch catch midge pupae as they rise through the water and before they reach the ducklings.

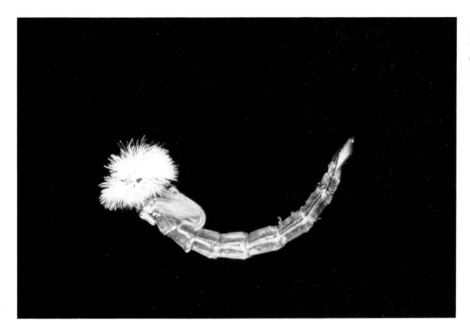

Midge pupa: Vital food for young ducklings. *Photo: Peter Gathercole*

invertebrates in a diet dominated by waterlice (*Asellus*), midge larvae, shrimps and mussels (see Figure 6.4). All three of these fish species were thought, therefore, to have the potential to influence mallard duckling survival by competing for vital insect food.

In 1987 we repeated our fish diet studies, sampling roach, bream, tench and perch through May, June and July, from both Main Lake and St Peter's Lake in the Wildfowl Reserve. The main results supported those from 1986 and are detailed for perch, bream and tench in Figures 6.5 to 6.9. Perch in both lakes specialise on midge pupae, catching them as they rise from the lake bed sediments towards the water surface prior to emergence. Clearly those pupae which are intercepted before reaching the surface are not available to dabbling ducks. This is a direct feeding overlap between fish and ducklings.

The bream in both St Peter's and Main Lake ate large numbers of larval chironomids and small bivalve molluscs (pea mussels, *Sphaerium sp.*) which they dug up from the lake bed sediments. Bream appear to select large midge larvae, (5mm and longer), chiefly those which are about to pupate prior to emergence. This represents an indirect diet overlap with dabbling ducklings because 0-14 day old mallard do not usually dig on the lake bed for midge larvae but eat adult midges taken from the water surface and bankside vegetation. Tufted duck of all ages, diving to feed on the lake bed, eat chironomid larvae and small mussels. Large numbers of these are also eaten by bream in both St Peter's and Main Lake: a direct diet overlap between bream and tufted duck. The bream suck up mouthfuls of silt, filter out and swallow the invertebrates, expelling the sediment through their gill rakers (bony comb-like projections on the gill arches).

Bream in the reserve Main Lake switch their feeding habits periodically between sediment digging for midge larvae, worms and pea mussels, and open water filter feeding on dense swarms of zooplankton (*Daphnia hyalina*) which occur throughout the summer. The dietary switching of bream occurs between years (primarily plankton in 1986, primarily benthic invertebrates in 1987). This has also been recorded by

Bream are largely lake bed feeders.

researchers in the Netherlands. Such behaviour makes it difficult to calculate accurately the likely impact of bream predation upon midge production.

Of the other fish species, tench – with their wide-ranging foraging behaviour – impinge on the diets of both dabbling and diving ducks, whilst roach in the Great Linford lakes have a smaller potential impact on the waterfowl by feeding largely on filamentous algae and *Daphnia* (waterfleas). Shoveler, a duck which filter-feeds on large *Daphnia* species, may be affected by roach which are likely to single out large crustaceans (eg *Daphnia magna*) as prey species.

Summary of fish feeding ecology at Linford.

● Perch in both lakes ate almost entirely midge pupae (Dipteran insects just about to hatch at the water surface; a key food resource for ducklings).

● Bream ate either *Daphnia* from the plankton or midge larvae and mussels on the lake bed.

● Tench ate either *Daphnia* (Main Lake) or, more usually, a wide variety of aquatic invertebrates (St Peter's Lake).

● Roach ate either *Daphnia* or filamentous algae.

● Perch, bream and, to a lesser extent, tench are in most direct competition with waterfowl for aquatic invertebrate food resources on the Great Linford gravel pits.

Table 6.1 Mean number (n = 20) with S.E., standard error) of benthic invertebrates per 0.05 m^2 in Main and St Peters Lakes.

		1986					
		May		June		July	
		Main	St Peters	Main	St Peters	Main	St Peters
Midges	*Diptera*	63(7)	23(3)	180(30)	18(4)	76(10)	14(3)
Worms	*Oligochaeta*	129(27)	24(5)	146(24)	44(10)	61(15)	36(11)
Water boatman	*Corixidae*	377(115)	4(1)	101(32)	5(1)	69(12)	9(2)
Snails	*Gastropoda*	2(0.2)	2(1)	3(1)	14(1.5)	4(1)	13(3)
Mussels	*Bivalvia*	3(1)	1(1)	2(0.5)	6(1)	5(2)	5(2)
Shrimps	*Amphipoda*	0	19(9)	0	11(2)	0	10(5)
Water lice	*Asellus*	0	5(1)	0	30(10)	0	43(5)
Mayflies	*Ephemeroptera*	0	8(1)	0	10(2)	0	2(1)
Caddis flies	*Trichoptera*	0	1(0.5)	0	1(0.2)	0	1(0.1)
Damsel flies	*Zygoptera*	0	3(1)	0	3(1)	0	3(1)
Alder flies	*Sialis*	0	1(0.2)	0	1(0.1)	0	9(2)

Table 6.2 Mean number (n = 20) with S.E., standard error) of benthic invertebrates per 0.05 m^2 in Main and St Peters.

		1987					
		May		June		July	
		Main	St Peters	Main	St Peters	Main	St Peters
Midges	*Diptera*	75(12)	18(3)	140(20)	28(3)	162(16)	27(3.5)
Worms	*Oligochaeta*	160(40)	64(5)	150(30)	70(18)	64(12)	74(18)
Water boatman	*Corixidae*	94(36)	1(0.75)	42(10)	15(6)	42(10)	20(8)
Snails	*Gastropoda*	4(1)	8(1)	2(1)	6(1.5)	4(0.5)	12(1)
Mussels	*Bivalvia*	10(3)	9(1)	7(1)	7.5(2)	11(3)	4(1)
Shrimps	*Amphipoda*	0	30(8)	0	19(4)	0	3(0.5)
Water lice	*Asellus*	0	6(1)	0	12(3)	0	19(3)
Mayflies	*Ephemroptera*	0	7(2)	0	26(4)	0	30(6)
Caddis flies	*Trichoptera*	0	2(0.5)	0	1(0.3)	0	0.2(0.1)
Damsel flies	*Zygoptera*	0	4(1)	0	4(1)	0	2(0.5)
Alder flies	*Sialis*	0	0.2(0.1)	0	1.5(0.1)	0	5(1)

Bream and tench in the net. Coarse fish removed from the lakes were sold to angling clubs

Now that we had demonstrated the feeding overlap between fish and ducks, we wanted to discover whether there were sufficient fish stocks in the Great Linford lakes to limit the availability of invertebrate food for wildfowl. We proposed to pump down Main Lake and St Peter's and net out the fish. This would allow us:

(1) To quantify the stocks and
(2) Remove the apparent food competition.

Two years of similar benthic invertebrate abundance data from the study lakes and two years of consistent fish diet data gave us the necessary baseline against which to compare future changes in the ecology of the lakes, so we proceeded to the second stage of this investigation – deciding to remove as many adult fish as possible from both study lakes.

In November 1987 the lakes were pumped down until the fish became concentrated in the deeper holes. These were then seine-netted and electro-fished (St Peter's). We then continued to monitor benthic invertebrate abundance on the lakes in 1988 and 1989 to assess any changes in the food available for ducklings. Table 6.3 gives the weights of fish of various species removed from the lakes.

It is important to note that under-yearling fish were not retained by the seine net and were not removed. These small fish, mostly roach and perch, are principally zooplankton feeders and should not have much impact upon larger invertebrates at this stage. These shoals of coarse fish fry provide food for piscivorous bird species such as kingfisher, goosander, heron, great crested grebe, little grebe and terns. Leaving them thus allowed the continued use of the lakes by fish-eating birds.

A total of over seven tonnes of fish was removed; the bulk being large specimens of bream (average 2kg), tench (1kg), and roach (0.5kg), which were sold for stocking coarse angling waters as far away as Newquay (Cornwall) and the East Anglian fens. The estimates of fish standing crop in our lakes allowed us to make some rough calculations on their likely food requirements.

Table 6.3 Summary of fish removed from Main Lake and St Peter's.

	Main Lake		St Peters Lake	
	Biomass in kg	Standing Crop kg/ha	Biomass in kg	Standing Crop kg/ha
Bream	3215	200	135	68
Roach	2844	178	230	115
Tench	8	0.5	205	103
Perch	286	18	11	5.5
Rudd	·	·	8.2	4.1
Carp	18	1.1	·	·
Pike	372	23	124	62
Totals	6743	420	713	355

For perch, a reasonable estimate of their food intake during June and July is 6% of their body weight per day. For Main Lake this means that perch would have eaten 17kg of food per day, or 0.1g per square metre per day. Emerging chironomids have a wet weight of approximately 0.005g, therefore the perch would account for 20 midges per square metre per day. In June 1987, when most ducklings hatched, the Main Lake insect emergence was around 80 midges per square metre per day and so the perch were taking about 20% of the emerging midges. In St Peter's, perch were eating 0.49kg of food per day or 0.024g per square metre per day. This is equivalent to 5 midges per square metre per day, 14% of the daily production. It is worth noting that despite large differences in perch density between the two study lakes, the impact of this fish on insect emergence was similar. Also, the impact calculated takes no account of the fact that some midges, eg *Chironomous cingulatus*, are nocturnal emergers and may not be available to either perch or ducklings, which we think feed exclusively between dawn and dusk.

In Main Lake, bream would eat around 7.5% of body weight per day through the summer or 200kg of invertebrate food per day. Two hundred kilograms of large midge larvae is equivalent to over 400 million organisms per day! At this rate (ie with all bream eating nothing but midge larvae) they would be removing about 11% per day. In St Peter's, adult bream would eat 9.76kg or 0.48g of invertebrates per square metre per day, also about 11% of the standing crop per day. As can be seen from Figures 6.3, 6.6 and 6.8, bream do not eat chironomid larvae alone but also pea mussels, oligochaete worms, water lice and *Daphnia*. In fact we estimate that, on average, midge larvae made up around 80% by weight of adult bream diet in Main Lake and 60% of their diet in St Peter's. The actual impact of bream predation upon larval midges during June and July is therefore of the order of 7% (St Peter's) or 9% (Main Lake) of larval midge biomass per day. This effect would be cumulative on the midge population through the early spring, although in the later months offset by growth and recruitment within the midge community, otherwise the midges would progressively decline. Some midge species can complete their life cycles in just a few weeks whilst other (larger) species may take up to two years.

Now that we had removed our fish, and reduced this predation pressure upon the larval midge populations, we predicted a corresponding increase in insect productivity and emergence which could improve duckling survival. However, Steve Cousins predicted that some competing predators of midges might increase to limit the midge production. In particular he

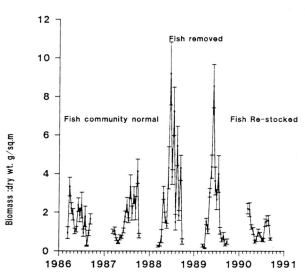

Figure 6.10 Biomass (weight) of midge larvae in Main Lake bottom samples showing increase after fish removal and decrease after fish re-stocking. Fish have a major effect on midge abundance.

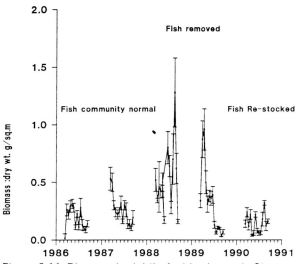

Figure 6.11 Biomass (weight) of midge larvae in St Peters Lake bottom samples showing increase after fish removal and decrease after fish re-stocking. Fish have a major effect on midge abundance.

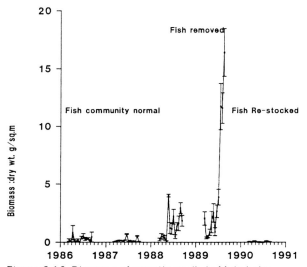

Figure 6.12 Biomass of aquatic snails in Main Lake bottom samples showing increase after fish removal and decrease after fish re-stocking. Fish have a major impact on snail abundance.

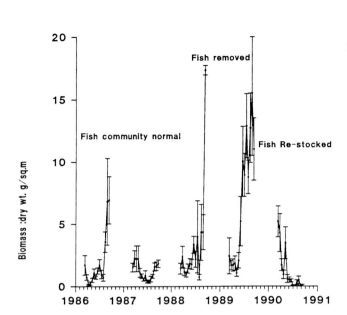

Figure 6.13 Biomass of aquatic snails in St Peters Lake bottom samples showing increase after fish removal and decrease after fish re-stocking. Fish have major impact on snail abundance.

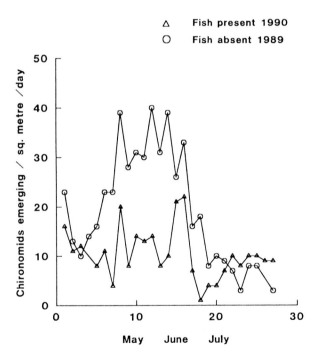

Figure 6.14 Numbers of midges hatching at the water surface were higher in St Peters Lake in 1989, after the fish removal than in 1990 when fish had been re-stocked.

cited the predatory invertebrates (alderfly larvae, damsel fly nymphs and leeches, all of which are common in St Peter's Lake. As we shall see, this did happen, but not to such an extent that the duckling invertebrate food supply was reduced back to the levels seen when the fish were present.

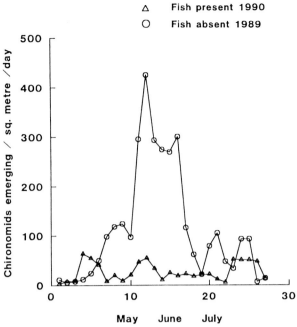

Figure 6.15 Numbers of midges hatching at the water surface were higher in Main Lake in 1989, after the fish removal than in 1990 when fish had been re-stocked.

The November 1987 fish removal allowed us to quantify our former fish stocks and calculate the impact of fish on the waterfowl food supply. The stock densities present translate into the following figures:

In the Main Lake, each square metre of lake bed was supporting on average 42 grammes of fish, whilst in St Peter's there was a standing crop of 35.5 grammes per square metre. This equated with the level expected in lakes of medium productivity and suggested that the fish removal should release a considerable surge of invertebrate productivity. Secondarily, the lack of disturbance of the lake bed after the removal of foraging bream and carp should allow the water to clear and promote the growth of submerged aquatic plants present in the seed bank. Any increased food supply, of either invertebrate or plant material would then potentially be available to waterfowl using the reserve lakes.

Invertebrate response to fish removal and subsequent re-stocking

Figures 6.10 to 6.13 give the mean biomass (with one standard error; grammes dry weight per square metre) of midge larvae and snails for both study lakes. It is clear in these four figures that fish removal promoted invertebrate production which was suppressed again after fish re-stocking. Figures 6.14 and 6.15 show how the numbers of midges emerging at the water surface (sampled in floating traps) were higher in both study lake sampling bays in 1989 (fish absent) than in 1990 (fish re-stocked in sampling bays).

Bream with mouth extended in feeding mode. Their digging behaviour keeps weed growth in check and reduces invertebrate abundance.

In addition, the invertebrate fauna of Main Lake became much more diverse after the fish were removed, with shrimps, water lice, mayfly nymphs, caddis larvae, alderfly larvae and other groups all colonising the 'de-fished' habitat.

The increase seen in alderfly numbers in each lake after the fish removal (Figures 6.16 and 6.17) could be due either to the reduction in predation by fish, an increase in midge food supply or a combination of these two effects. Abundant alderfly populations will eat large numbers of larval midges and we are experimenting with tench to see whether their selective predation on alderfly larvae will suppress this predatory invertebrate, leaving more midges for the birds.

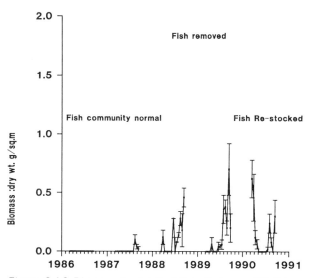

Figure 6.16 Biomass (weight) of Alderfly larvae (*Sialis*) in Main Lake bottom samples showing increase after fish removal and decrease after fish re-stocking.

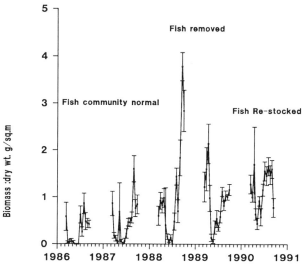

Figure 6.17 Biomass (weight) of Alderfly larvae (*Sialis*) in St Peters Lake bottom samples showing increase after fish removal and decrease after fish re-stocking.

Experimental ponds were used to confirm the result of the fish removal.

A large species of water flea (*Daphnia magna*) appeared in Main Lake after the fish removal. It is likely that this species was formerly excluded by fish predation and is now available as food for shoveler, a duck which filters large zooplankton species from the water with its specialised bill.

Experimental Ponds

It could be argued that the changes described above are due simply to co-incidental year on year variations in invertebrate abundance and weed growth in the reserve lakes. For this reason, in 1986 we dug a series of 10 experimental ponds which were left fallow in 1987 to mature. In 1988 we split each pond in half with a netting partition and stocked one half of nine of the ponds with fish, leaving the other half as a fish-free control. The tenth pond was left fish-free in both halves as a check on the equality of the halves of a single pond. Of the nine ponds which we stocked with fish, three contained perch, three bream and three perch and bream.

The insect emergence from all 20 pond halves was monitored throughout the summer and the benthic invertebrate populations were sampled in the autumn. Overall, both perch and bream significantly reduced aquatic invertebrate abundance in the ponds, showing in a controlled experiment that the changes seen in the reserve lakes are not due to chance alone. The tenth pond, with no fish in either half, had similar levels of insect abundance in both halves throughout the sampling programme. This controlled experiment confirmed the results of our fish manipulations in the Great Linford reserve lakes.

Coarse fish in gravel pit nature reserves.

The Great Linford gravel pits supported between 350 and 420kg/ha of coarse fish, or around 35-45 grammes per square metre. This is a relatively high biomass (standing crop) of fish, indicating that these man-made lakes can develop within 20 years of digging into prolific fisheries. Hard-bedded pits which were dry-dug tend to make very good tench fisheries, whilst soft-bedded wet-dug lakes tend to support large populations of bream and carp.

For the conservation of wildlife other than fish we recommend regular fish removals (say every 3 to 5 years) from reserve lakes. This will serve to stimulate invertebrate and water plant production, leading to good quality habitat for breeding waterfowl and a diverse array of other animal species including amphibians, dragonflies and many smaller insect groups. Aquatic snails, which are an important food for diving ducks, increase greatly when fish are removed.

Fish removed from reserve lakes can readily be sold through dealers and angling clubs to generate an income for further nature reserve management and improved sport for coarse fishermen elsewhere.

Food competition in the bream populations at Great Linford

The fish community of Main Lake was dominated in weight terms by bream (48%) and roach (42%). St Peter's Lake was dominated by tench (29%), roach (32%) and bream (19%).

The bream populations in the two lakes have been studied since 1982. The age structure shows that the production of young bream is very variable from year to year. The most abundant year classes were found to be those produced in 1973, 1975 and 1976, which were years with particularly warm summers. As bream are long-lived fish that often do not mature until they are around seven years old, the 1973, 1975 and 1976 year classes still formed most of the spawning adult population in 1987/88, as summers from 1977 to 1981 were relatively poor.

In 1982, the growth of these year classes of bream was considered to be fairly good (Figure 6.18) compared to other waters, but during the next five years they showed very little further growth. In 1982, the mean length was 430mm and mean weight was 1.2kg (2.6lbs). In 1987, the mean length was 440mm with a mean weight of 1.5 kg (3.3lbs). In the Netherlands it has been recorded that low numbers of chironomids result in poor bream growth. In 1987, the average chironomid standing crop in the wildfowl reserve Main Lake (see Table 6.4) was 10.6 grammes per square metre, a rather low figure. In other words, Main Lake bream were probably stunted through intense competition for food.

In 1988, when the population density of bream had been reduced by the fish removal, the average standing crop of chironomids increased to 20.8 grammes per square metre (Table 6.4). The lakes were netted again in November 1988 and only 32 kilogrammes per hectare of bream were caught, compared to 158 kilogrammes per hectare the previous year. These bream, which we had missed in the 1987 netting, had shown an almost incredible change in their growth rate. Mean length increased to 470mm and mean weight increased to 2.2kg (4.8lbs) which meant that the bream which had grown very little for the previous five years had increased their weight by an average of 0.7kg (1.5lbs) in just one growing season! This increase seems to be a direct response to the amount of food available and indicates the efficiency of bream at cropping the surge in chironomid production.

Figure 6.18 Smoothed average lengths for a given age of Main Lake bream.

Table 6.4. Average biomass (g^{m-2}) of chironomid larvae in Main Lake from March-October 1986 and 1987 (before fish removal) and 1988 and 1989 (after fish removal).

Year	Average biomass (g m^{-2})		S.E. (Standard Error)	Range
1986	Wet	11.00	1.41	1.92-21.42
	Dry	1.59	0.20	0.29-3.10
	AFDW	1.15	0.15	0.21-2.24
1987	Wet	10.60	1.71	2.45-23.02
	Dry	1.53	0.25	0.35-3.30
	AFDW	1.11	0.18	0.26-2.41
1988	Wet	20.77	4.68	1.75-64.2
	Dry	3.00	0.67	0.25-9.26
	AFDW	2.17	0.49	0.19-6.70
1989	Wet	15.94	4.31	1.05-59.56
	Dry	2.30	0.62	0.15-8.59
	AFDW	1.67	0.45	0.11-6.22

(Note, AFDW = Ash-free dry weight ie the weight of organic matter

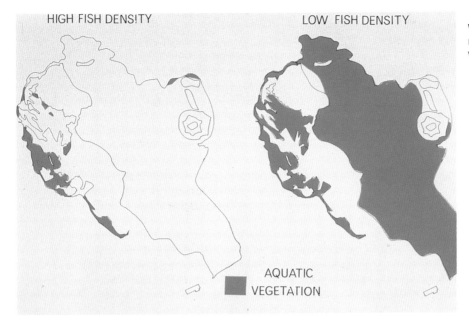

HIGH FISH DENSITY   LOW FISH DENSITY

Weed growth in the
reserve lakes with and
without fish

AQUATIC
VEGETATION

Effects of coarse fish on aquatic vegetation

The reduction in bream density brought about remarkable changes in the aquatic vegetation in both lakes, but especially Main Lake. For the previous 25 years Main Lake had very little aquatic vegetation, but after the fish removal, aquatic plants colonised the whole bed very quickly. This effect is shown by the data from the fortnightly sampling programmes both on Main Lake and St Peter's Lake (Figures 6.19 and 6.20). Fennel-leaved pondweed and Canadian pondweed covered almost the entire lake in one season.

Bream feed mainly by winnowing the bottom sediments for chironomids and this causes increased turbidity of the water which reduces light penetration and hence plant growth. The high density of bream in Main Lake seems to have been responsible for holding back the weed growth. Carp are also reported to have a similar effect in other lakes. In St Peter's Lake, where the bream density was much lower and the substrate firmer than in Main Lake, aquatic plants were already well established. However, after the fish were removed submerged weed beds also increased considerably in this lake. Roach eat plant seedlings and may also have had a suppressing effect on the weed beds. We cannot be sure whether weed suppression was due mainly to bream, roach or a combination of the two but evidence from other studies indicates that the bream are probably the principal culprits.

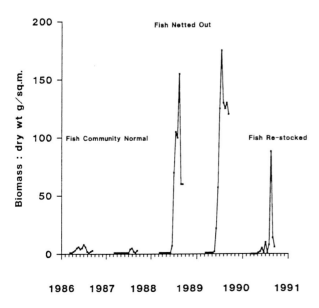

Figure 6.19 Biomass (weight) of water weeds in Main Lake bottom samples showing increase after fish removal and decrease after fish re-stocking.

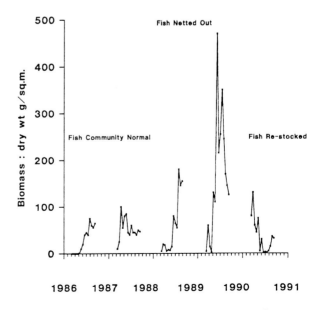

Figure 6.20 Biomass (weight) of water weeds in St Peters Lake bottom samples showing increase after fish removal and decrease after fish re-stocking.

Fish or ducks: the decision must be made as to whether a given lake is principally a wildlife conservation area or a coarse fishery.

After fish were reintroduced to the St Peter's and Main Lake sampling bays, the abundance of submerged plant growth declined in both (Figures 6.19 and 6.20), starting to reverse the proliferation stimulated by the fish removal.

Our results indicate, therefore, that coarse fish suppress the feeding habitat quality for wildfowl in two important ways:

1   They reduce the food available to young dabbling ducklings and adult ducks by decreasing the abundance and variety of aquatic invertebrates, (see Chapter 2).

2   They suppress submerged plant growth by eating plant seedlings (roach), uprooting germinating seeds and making the water turbid through their active digging on the lake bed (bream, carp and, to a lesser extent, tench) see Chapter 4.

Bream and carp populations dig over the beds of lakes throughout summer and autumn in their constant search for invertebrate foods – midge larvae, worms and pea mussels. By keeping the sediments in constant movement the fish release nutrients from the mud which fuel the growth of phytoplankton in the lakes, turning them green or brown. These algal blooms also serve to limit the growth of submerged weed beds, both by competing for nutrients with the larger plants and by cutting off their supply of sunlight. Bream and carp at high population densities are therefore deleterious to the overall conservation value of lakes. The decision must be made as to whether a given lake is principally a wildlife conservation area (with *low* fish stocks) or a coarse fishery (usually deliberately stocked to make the angling more productive).

A species of fish which is much less destructive of aquatic plants is the tench. Moderately dense tench populations will live in well-weeded gravel pits (like St Peter's lake at Great Linford) and thrive by picking invertebrates like *Asellus*, snails, mussels, midge larvae, *Sialis* larvae, caddis larvae, and shrimps from plant surfaces and from the lake bed. Tench also spawn on weed beds and so the populations of tench and plants are able to co-exist because tench are much less active 'diggers' of lake beds than either bream or carp. Gravel pits make excellent tench fisheries and can be successfully managed as such, but if large numbers of carp are introduced, the weed beds disappear and with them go the tench.

Coarse fish and aquatic weed control

Our results show that fish can be used to "biomanipulate" weed bed growth. If the intention in managing a lake is to promote weed growth for wildlife, then net out adult bream and carp (and probably roach), all of which can suppress seedling establishment and growth.

If the intention is to suppress weed growth (eg on sailing or water-skiing lakes) then rather than using expensive chemical weed-killers or manual cutting, simply stock with a high density of adult bream or carp (to a combined standing crop of 400-500kg/ha) and watch the weed beds decline and, especially on soft-bedded lakes, disappear. Note that the resulting lake conditions will be markedly turbid and prone to algal blooms in summer.

If you wish to have fish in a well-weeded lake, we recommend using perch, pike and tench to a combined standing crop of around 200kg/ha, this should produce the desired effect on most gravel pit lakes. More research is needed to refine this potentially potent and environmentally-friendly form of weed bed management.

The tench population of St Peter's Lake

The fish removal in 1987 provided a rare opportunity to study an unstocked and unfished tench population which had been subject only to natural influences for a period of 20 years or so. Despite the great popularity of tench as an angler's quarry, very little research had been carried out on the species in the UK. Main Lake, which was virtually weed-free prior to 1987, had very few tench (around one individual per three hectares) whilst the weedy St Peter's lagoons supported a thriving population of around 176 individuals per hectare (102.2kg/ha). Since so little information was available on tench biology we (Wright & Giles, 1991) decided to examine the basic aspects of population biology: age structure, life span, and growth rates for males and females. Tench were aged mostly from scales, but a small sub-sample was also aged from reading prepared opercular bones (gill covers) and otoliths (inner ear bones). Otoliths provided the clearest growth rings on fish of nine years or older, on younger fish both scales and opercular bones were satisfactory structures for ageing. The oldest fish captured during the study was 15 years of age. The growth of males and females is detailed in Figures 6.21 and 6.22.

The figures show how female and male tench grow steadily in average weight with age and how their instantaneous growth rates drop progressively as they age. Note how much heavier females of a given age are than males. On average, it takes a female St Peter's tench 10 years to reach a weight of around 1kg, whilst males need around 12 years to reach the same weight. Both sexes have a similar potential life span of 14-15 years. The average length (mm) for tench of both sexes at a given age is shown in Figure 6.23. Figure 6.24 gives the size structure for the male and female tench population, judged from fish removed in

Tench appear to compete with wildfowl less than other fish species.

Figure 6.21 Growth in weight of male St Peters Lake tench with age and simultaneous decline in specific (instantaneous) growth rate.

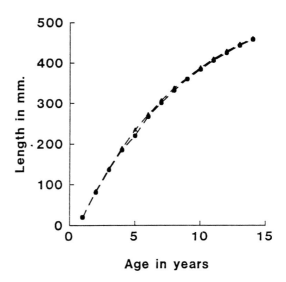

Figure 6.23 Smoothed average lengths for a given age of male and female St Peters Lake tench.

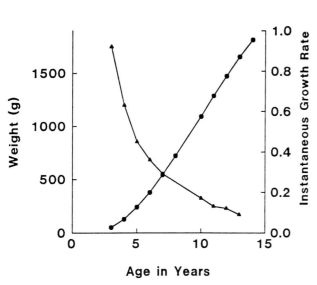

Figure 6.22 Growth in weight of female St Peters Lake tench with age and simultaneous decline in specific (instantaneous) growth rate.

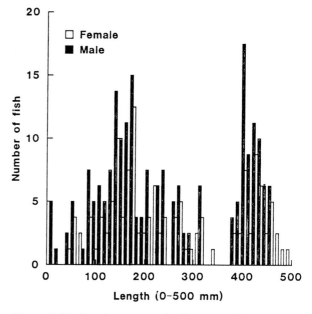

Figure 6.24 Size-frequency distribution of St Peters Lake tench showing variable recruitment with many 400mm fish but, for instance, very few 300mm fish. Tench produce large numbers of surviving young only in very warm summers.

1987. (Similar numbers of tench were removed in a repeat operation in 1988). Note especially how the size classes of fish are unevenly represented, indicating good and bad spawning years.

Success of reproduction in a given year is termed 'year class strength' and this has been related in Table 6.5 to water temperatures (degree days > 16°C from the nearby Grafham Water reservoir) for the St Peter's tench stock.

As can be seen, in general relatively warm years gave rise to prolific tench year classes. In warm weather young cyprinid fish larvae grow quickly and probably have better survival than in cool years when their food supply is less abundant.

Table 6.5

Year Class	No. in Year Class	No. degree days
		> 16°C
1985	117	131
1984	184	Missing data
1983	70	Missing data
1982	101	178
1981	73	128
1980	32	86
1979	16	143
1978	33	71
1977	89	49
1976	247	328
1975	304	255

The ecology of gravel pit pike populations

Pike prey upon the fish which compete with the wildfowl for food. They also occasionally take ducklings. They can therefore have both positive and negative effects in wildfowl reserves. Wright (1988) described our diet studies on pike at Great Linford as follows:

A stomach sampler for live fish (Giles, 1980) was constructed using an irrigating syringe with rubber tubing attached to the nozzle. Pike were anaesthetized with benzocaine and the rubber tubing was passed through the pyloric sphincter. Water was then passed from the syringe into the stomach until it had an inflated appearance. The tube was then withdrawn and the water and stomach contents expressed by firmly passing a hand along the ventral side of the fish. This method is now well tried and is not thought to cause the pike any harm or significant distress.

A total of 135 stomach samples were taken from pike in Main Lake and 277 from pike in St Peter's during 1986/87. This was before most fish were removed from the two lakes in November 1987. A large proportion of the fish sampled had empty stomachs (78% in Main Lake and 84% in St Peter's). This has been found by several other researchers when studying the diet of pike. Figure 6.25 shows the composition of the diet; each food item is shown in the pie-charts as the percentage of all items consumed. In Main Lake, prey species included adult roach, perch, roach × bream hybrids, pike, bleak and 0+ group roach and bream (ie those in their first year). Two pike caught in June and July each contained a mallard duckling. In St Peter's

Lake, the prey species included roach, perch, bream, pike, tench and bullheads.

The most common species found in the diet of pike in both lakes was roach. Several studies (eg by Richard Mann of The Institute of Freshwater Ecology) have reached the conclusion that pike are opportunist fish eaters which prey chiefly upon the more abundant and vulnerable species in a particular habitat. This appears to be the case in Main Lake and St Peter's, where roach are more abundant than perch. Although Main Lake had a large biomass of bream (158 kilograms per hectare) and St Peter's a large biomass of tench (96kg/ha), most of these fish were over 400mm in length and therefore available only to the largest pike. It has been suggested that prey one quarter to one third of the body length of a pike are optimal, although large pike continue to eat small prey. Sample sizes in the present study were rather too small to draw many conclusions about seasonal changes in prey selection. The box overleaf summarises details used in calculating the annual consumption and prey selection by pike.

Main Lake

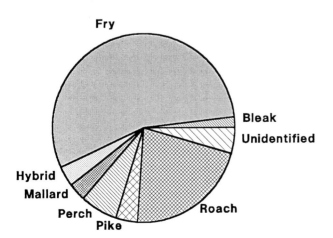

St. Peters

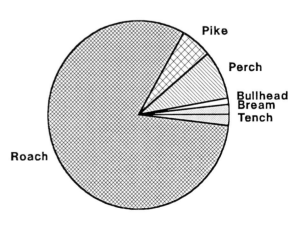

Figure 6.25 Pie charts showing composition of Main Lake and St Peters Lake pike diets. Roach were the commonest prey species in both lakes.

Annual food consumption of pike

The annual food consumption (C) of pike was estimated using a formula:

$$C = B \times R + P \times E$$

Where B is the mean biomass of pike (kg)
P is the annual production (kg)
R is the annual maintenance coefficient (1.73)
E is the efficiency of food utilisation (2.167).

The values for R and E used were those calculated by Richard Mann. The mean biomass of pike in Main Lake in 1987 was 19.88kg/ha and production was estimated at 8kg/ha. This results in an annual food consumption of 51kg/ha, about one third of the standing crop of roach and perch! In St Peter's, the mean biomass was 51kg/ha with a production of 20kg/ha. This results in an annual food consumption of 132kg/ha. The standing crop of roach and perch, excluding 0+ group fish, is less than this figure, so predation on species other than roach and perch is also important in the diet of pike.

Table 6.6 shows the percentages of fish species in St Peter's Lake that were removed by electrofishing in November 1987. These figures can be compared with the percentages of fish species found in the pikes' stomachs. An electivity value can be calculated which is a measure of the selectivity by a predator for a particular prey. Positive values indicate that pike are selecting a prey species.

Table 6.6. The percentage number of fish in St Peter's Lake (p), the percentage number of fish found in pike stomachs (r) and electivity values (s) calculated from $s = (r \cdot p)/(r + p)$. (A positive number indicates prey selection.)

SPECIES	% no. in lake	% no. found in pike stomachs	S
PIKE	4.3	5.6	0.13
ROACH	70.8	83.0	0.08
PERCH	7.3	7.4	−0.007
BREAM	2.0	2.0	0
TENCH	5.6	2.0	−0.47

Cannibalism in pike

In St Peter's, pike positively selected roach and other pike to eat. Pike were the preferred species, which emphasized the importance of cannibalism in the diet. Cannibalism may account for most of the natural mortality of pike in the first two years of life and continue to be important as the fish grow older. Even a low frequency of occurrence may be important to the pike population if cannibalism acts over a long period of time. Often, it seems, that the predator becomes the prey!

Pike population dynamics

There remains much to be discovered about the population dynamics of pike and in particular the key factors affecting growth rates and population structure and the importance of cannibalism. The early life history has been studied very little and this is where

Cannibalism in pike fry (Photo: Peter Gathercole)

A pike with a duckling in its mouth. The interaction between the species is complex.

The removal of large pike from a lake might increase the numbers of smaller fish.

the answer to population control may lie. Female pike produce huge quantities of eggs (25 000 per kg body weight) and very large numbers of pike fry may hatch. Under natural conditions pike egg densities are often 30-40 per m^2 but they can rise to 10 000 eggs per m^2. There is often greater than 99% mortality during the first few weeks of life, so mortality at this stage will largely determine the number of adult pike produced in a given year (ie. the year class strength).

Since little was known about the factors affecting numbers of pike fry, we conducted a series of tank and pond experiments to gain some information about the effects of population density on pike fry survival and growth.

25 000 pike fry were hatched from eggs stripped mainly from two females and these were placed at different densities in a series of tank and pond experiments. Densities ranged from 1 to 82 per m^2 in the ponds and 80 to 1076 per m^2 in the tanks. Pike fry in the tanks were given food *ad lib* and were free from

non-cannibalistic predation. Pike fry in the ponds were subject to natural predators (eg great diving beetle larvae, herons, etc.) but no adult pike were present. The tank experiments showed pike fry survival to be density-dependent and cannibalism to be important as a cause of mortality in the higher densities. Those pike which became cannibalistic had the fastest growth rates.

Although the pond experiments confirmed that pike fry survival was density-dependent (Figure 6.26), percentage survival was lower than in the tank experiments, possibly because of the additional non-cannibal predation. The numbers and biomass of pike at the end of the experiment in each of the sectored ponds did not vary greatly considering the range of original densities stocked. Growth rates in both ponds were extremely variable (the range in size at the end of the year was 99 to 287mm) although Pond 2 produced larger numbers of smaller pike. Roughly equal numbers of pike over 200mm were produced in each of the two ponds and this did not seem to be related to initial stocking

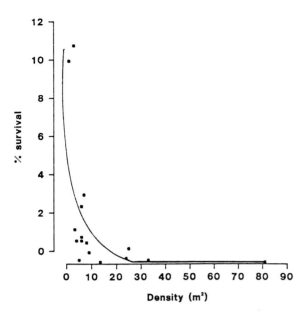

Figure 6.26 Density-dependent survival of pike fry. The proportion of young pike surviving to the end of their first summer declines steeply with increasing population density. Survival improves rapidly at initial densities below 10 fry per square metre.

density. The pike had apparently regulated their own numbers, with the largest fish being cannibals.

Without predation from adult pike, it is apparent that large numbers of young pike survive. The mean number produced in Pond 1 was 604 pike per hectare and in Pond 2 was 1165 pike per hectare. Cannibalism took place between the young pike but survival was still relatively high.

Cannibalism occurs in the pike of both of the Wildfowl Reserve lakes: 6% of pike stomach contents from Main Lake and 3% of those from St Peter's were pike. This difference in the incidence of cannibalism may be attributable to the fact that in Main Lake there was very little plant cover and in St Peter's there is a high density of small pike.

Many pike bear scars which indicate that they have been attacked by other pike. It is possible that the removal of large pike could increase the survival of smaller pike. If so, a greater number of smaller pike may lead to increased duckling predation, as it is these fish which occupy the duckling habitat.

Main Lake and St Peter's lake had very different pike populations – the weed free open water of Main Lake in the early 1980s contained many large pike, whilst the weedy shallows of St Peter's had a population of mostly small pike. The Figure 6.27 shows the percentage size frequency distributions for the two populations.

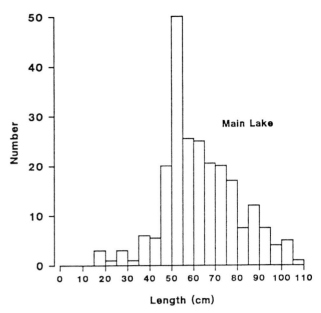

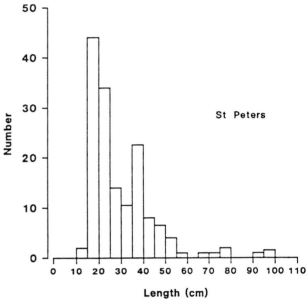

Figure 6.27 Percentage size-frequency distributions for Main Lake and St Peters Lake pike populations. Note that Main Lake fish tend to be much larger than St Peters fish.

We were interested in the reasons why the structure of the pike populations of these two lakes was so different. The answers lie in the early survival and recruitment of young pike. To find out more about this, the survival of pike fry in Main Lake and St Peter's was monitored. The average density of (patchily-distributed) eggs found in Main Lake in April was 83/m². Hatching success of these was extremely low, probably because of silting of the eggs after a series of gales. A total of only three juvenile pike was caught during the entire summer of 1986 and there were certainly less than 10 per hectare. Main Lake contained very little plant cover and very young pike are easily predated by larger pike and possibly other fish. In contrast, in St Peter's the survival of young pike was relatively good. By the end of the summer the density of surviving pike fry was estimated at 373 per hectare. The main reason for these differences in the densities of young pike is thought to be the lack of suspended silt in St Peter's and the greater amount of aquatic vegetation. The highest numbers of pike fry were found in dense weed beds.

The shallow, weedy conditions that are ideal for the survival of pike fry are not so good for them once they grow older because prey capture is often difficult and, in shallow water, summer temperatures may rise above the pike's optimum for growth.

Breeding success of pike

In 1987, a study of the reproductive success of pike was carried out. The population fecundity (ie the total number of eggs produced) was estimated to be approximately 6.4 million in Main Lake and 1.5 million in St Peter's.

Survival of the eggs in Main Lake was assessed at three stages during development and it was estimated that there was a 95% loss between spawning and hatching. The weather during spawning was calm and it was anticipated that the survival of pike fry would be relatively good in Main Lake following the experience of 1986.

During the fish removal experiment in 1987, all pike caught were measured, weighed, sexed and scales were taken for ageing. The pike removed were used for stocking waters elsewhere. The total number of adult pike (one year and over) caught in Main Lake was 64 females and 46 males. The total biomass of pike in Main Lake was 322kg (ie 19kg per hectare) This was approximately 5% of the total fish population by weight.

The survival of 1987 pike fry had been relatively good in both lakes. There was a total of 113 0 + pike caught in Main Lake (seven per hectare) and 46 from St Peter's (23 per hectare). However, these figures show that less than five in 100 000 pike eggs survive to become yearlings in both Main Lake and St Peter's.

The age structure of the population in the two lakes is shown in Figure 6.28. The pike in Main Lake appear to be longer lived than in St Peter's. Mortality rates in Main Lake are, on average, 19% per year for females and 23% for males; while in St Peter's they are 32.6% for females and 29.5% for males. The pike population of Main Lake showed much more variability in year class strength than that of St Peter's, probably reflecting weather effects such as the 1986 gales on the more exposed Main Lake.

The growth of pike from the two lakes is shown in Figure 6.29. Pike in Main Lake have a higher length

Nick Giles sampling pike eggs in early spring

105

A catch of pike in a fyke net

for age than those in St Peter's. Female pike in both lakes are generally faster growing and longer lived than males; this accounts for their larger average size. The oldest pike found in both lakes were 13 years old,

but few pike in either lake were more than 10 years old. Although pike fry survival in St Peter's appears to be good, the shallow, weedy conditions are less than ideal for the older pike, which prefer more open water. This is reflected in their slower growth rates and higher mortality.

Understanding the ways in which pike populations are influenced by ecological conditions is obviously useful in predicting the responses of pike to changes in their habitat and management practices.

Pike populations in gravel pits

Shallow, well-weeded pits will tend to contain large numbers of relatively small pike. Open-watered pits will harbour large pike and cannibalism will be frequent. It is the relatively small (< 5 pounds) adult pike living around the weeded littoral zones of lakes, which eat waterfowl most often. To improve juvenile waterfowl production, *small* pike can easily be netted out from reserve lakes.

Large (> 15 pound) pike may be best left in wildfowl reserves since, through cannibalism, they are likely to exert a degree of control over the numbers of their smaller (duckling-eating) brethren. They also eat other fish species which compete with ducks for food.

More research is needed to examine this question in detail. Practical experience on many waters has shown, however, that when most large pike are removed from a lake there is an 'explosion' of young pike surviving subsequently. Pike are easily captured in fyke nets set close to weedy shallows in March/April, when the adult fish congregate for spawning.

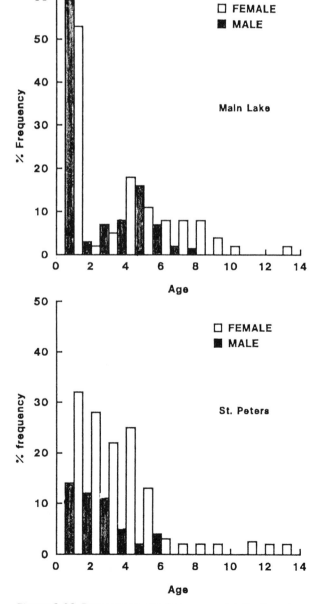

Figure 6.28 Percentage age-frequency distributions for Main Lake and St Peters Lake pike populations.

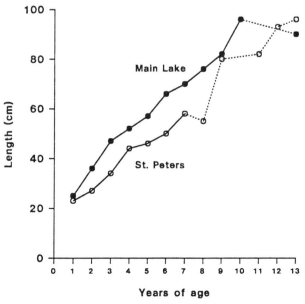

Figure 6.29 The growth in length of Main Lake and St Peters Lake pike with age. Main Lake fish are larger, especially early in life (2-8 years of age.)

Gravel pits as angling waters

Fish removed from waterfowl conservation areas can be used to stock purpose-made coarse fisheries. There are three principal types of coarse fishery popular with today's anglers:

1. Specimen carp waters

These are stocked with up to 800kg/ha of adult carp (both common and mirror carp), often including fish of over 10kg in weight. Heavily stocked carp lakes of this type are very popular with 'specimen-hunting' anglers who will pay £200 or more per season to fish syndicated waters (1992 prices). Some carp fisheries are run on a lucrative day ticket basis, charging around £5 per rod per day. If permission is gained from English Nature and the NRA to stock catfish (Wels) in self-contained waters, the attraction of the fishery will be all the greater. Such lakes are of high amenity value for angling but have little other conservation value.

2. Match fisheries

Bream and roach are the prime quarry of the stillwater match angler who wishes to fish competitively for shoaling fish and amass a large catch at the end of a given match day. Bream and roach can be successfully stocked into match waters to provide good sport and most gravel pits are able to support a combined stock density of 300-400kg/ha. The aim of match fishery lake management is to provide a large number of similar fishing positions ('pegs') where there is an equal chance of any angler making a good catch. This minimises the importance of drawing a 'good peg' at the start of the match and allows fishing skill to determine the outcome of the competition. Good match waters are, therefore, rather uniform with few localised fish-holding features (eg food-rich hollows, weed beds, inflowing streams etc).

3. General coarse fisheries

These waters are managed to provide an intermediate form of fishing between 'specimen' and 'match' fisheries. The species generally sought by coarse fishermen who are happy to catch a mixed bag during a day are tench, perch, roach, rudd, bream, crucian carp and an occasional pike. Winter specimen pike fishing is often available on such lakes and large fish can be stocked to ensure the presence of several heavyweight specimens if the lake is large enough to support them. The fact that high densities of carp and bream are usually absent from these waters means that submerged plant growth is sometimes substan-

tial and, if suitable wet boggy areas and pools are created around the lake edges, the overall conservation value of such fisheries can be considerable. A high number of fish species is combined with good invertebrate diversity and a reasonable abundance of dragonflies and other high amenity value groups. The peripheral pools and bogs will support amphibians, grass snakes and a wide diversity of water edge-nesting birds. Most anglers enjoy fishing in pleasant surroundings where they have a good chance of observing wildlife at close quarters.

Put-and-take trout fisheries

Gravel pit trout fisheries are ideal put-and-take waters, providing inexpensive fishing for large numbers of day ticket and syndicate anglers. Rainbow trout are the most usual species and are generally stocked at around 200 fish to the hectare. Some small specialist fisheries stock very large (up to 10kg) rainbow trout and charge up to £40 per day to fish for them. Where fish of 0.5-1kg are the norm and a bag limit of four to six fish is imposed, most waters charge £15-£20 for day tickets. Some small waters are syndicated and stocked according to members' requirements. Excessive weed growth is a common problem in both gravel pit trout and sailing lakes. It is usually dealt with by the application of herbicides (see Chapter 7) but the stocking of grass carp, which eat soft water plants, or common carp, which uproot water weeds, are useful alternative methods of biological weed control. Carp stocked into sailing lakes for weed control could be netted out five years later at a much larger size and sold to stock angling waters. Such fish would be replaced with smaller specimens to continue the cycle. This combination of extensive fish-farming coupled with aquatic plant

Put-and-take trout fisheries are increasingly popular.

107

Electro-fishing in St Peter's Lake. Licences are often needed for fish removal and reintroduction programmes.

control is of course the converse of removing fish from waterfowl conservation lakes.

An understanding of the ecology of our native freshwater fish can be useful for many lake management purposes. The production of large tench and carp is particularly worthwhile for income generation as both species are in great demand from angling clubs and coarse fishery managers.

With good planning, on large sites (eg The Cotswold Water Park) each of these types of coarse fishery can be developed close by other lakes managed specifically for wildfowl conservation.

Gravel pit fisheries

The management of freshwater fisheries is an art incorporating an increasing amount of science. A competent fisheries biologist should be contracted to carry out an initial stock survey of a given lake to include a best estimate of abundance (high, medium, low) and measures of growth, recruitment success and body condition of the principal fish species. If the decision is taken to remove fish and transfer them to another water, representative samples of each species must be taken (alive) to a fish diseases expert (NRA, MAFF, independent consultant) for health certification.

If the stocks are certified healthy, a fisheries biologist will be needed to assess the best method of catching the fish (fyke netting, seine netting, electro-fishing, etc.), to determine whether pumping down the lake is worthwhile and to ensure that the fish are well handled and stored (eg in floating cages) prior to collection by fish dealers or fishing club personnel. Large coarse fish are valuable (eg at current retail prices of £6-8 per kilo). Lakes should be netted when the water is relatively cool (late autumn/early spring) when weed beds have died back and fish are least likely to be distressed by low oxygen concentrations. Netting and holding fish in high summer often leads to excessive mortality.

Non-specialists are strongly advised to take advice either from an organisation such as The Game Conservancy or from their regional National Rivers Authority (NRA) staff. Do not forget that consents are often needed to catch and move fish from one lake to another.

Main Lake bream
awaiting transportation
to an angling water
in Cornwall

Fisheries biology: conclusions

The results from the 20-year ARC/Game Conservancy project have shown how coarse fish colonise flooded mineral workings and subsequently thrive. This is true for both silty, wet-dug pits which tend to be bream-dominated and clear water, hard-bedded, dry-dug lakes which tend to be tench-dominated. In both lake types, fish have been shown to compete successfully for invertebrate foods (especially midges and snails) with a variety of waterfowl. Young ducklings suffer most from this food competition. Fish also suppress the growth of submerged weed beds, particularly in wet-dug lakes. This limits dramatically the food available for herbivorous waterfowl such as gadwall, swans and coot. The removal of most adult fish from the ARC Wildfowl Reserve lakes led directly to increased habitat use and improved survival of tufted ducklings and major increases in winter wildfowl use of the lakes. Breeding duck diversity also increased after the removal of the fish .

The fish populations appear to be affected by weather in fundamental ways. Tench and bream need warm summers to produce abundant year classes of fry whilst pike in silty lakes need settled conditions in April to allow successful incubation of their eggs.

It would appear that bream dominate the wet-dug lake ecosystems: By turning over the sediments in

their constant search for food they root up weed seedlings and fuel algal blooms by releasing plant nutrients. This can be changed fundamentally by removing the bream. The lake settles and clears, weeds germinate successfully and grow, further stabilising the sediments. The deep layer of inorganic silt on the lake bed becomes bound and consolidated in the long term. If enough carp or bream are then stocked into this system, the lake will revert to its former state. This is a prime example of how lakes can be managed by biological techniques (biomanipulated) to achieve desired end points (eg improved wildfowl breeding success in the case of Great Linford). Different sites will have different ecological problems to solve in establishing the best management procedures, but the fish/duck food competition story is likely to have far-reaching implications in future wetland management programmes.

In achieving the goal of better duckling survival at Great Linford, our research team has also produced a great deal of useful background information on coarse fish populations, particularly pike, bream and tench. This will be useful for the better management of coarse fisheries on those lakes where angling is the principal recreational activity. Of all the fish species studied, tench appear to have the best potential to live in wildfowl reserves at fairly high stock densities without devastating either the weeds or the invertebrate food supply for wildfowl.

CHAPTER 7

HABITAT MANAGEMENT FOR A DIVERSE BIOLOGICAL COMMUNITY

Habitat destruction worldwide is resulting in the loss of species of plants and animals and a shrinking of the complex web of nature. Wetlands are among the most threatened habitats on earth. Remaining wildlife habitat thus requires careful long-term management. It is not, however, sufficient to protect remaining fragments; man can create wetlands to increase the resource for the future. On man-made sites intended as nature reserves, leaving nature to its own devices will merely lead to areas dominated by a few strongly competitive plant and animal species. The careful establishment and maintenance of a diverse botanical mosaic is what is needed. If this mosaic is to harbour the best mix of high conservation value species, it must be soundly designed and managed, and based on an intimate knowledge of habitat ecology.

At wetland sites, an ability to control water levels allows the long-term management of shallow ponds and pools for amphibians and macro-invertebrates (eg dragonflies). Such ponds at Great Linford harbour rare (and protected) great crested newts as well as a wide variety of dragonfly and damselfly species.

The management of a reserve for wildfowl conservation will, if it is done properly, give rise to very rich plant and animal communities which will include some rarities. The soft-bedded gravel pits at Great Linford have proved to be ideal habitats for spined loach (*Cobitis taenia*); a species which is restricted to southeast England and which is referred to in the Council for Europe's 'Threatened Freshwater Fishes of Europe' as being rare. Nobody could have predicted that such a rare fish species would thrive in man-made lakes but the non-intensive use of the Great Linford site as a whole has allowed it to survive so far.

The ornithological interest of the Great Linford reserve is underlined by the sighting of a substantial total of 189 bird species (70 breeding at least once) on an area which was in the recent past, completely dug-out and remodelled in the search for building materials.

In achieving its aim, to create good wildfowl habitat and improve duck breeding success in new gravel pits, the project at Great Linford has also resulted in the development of an excellent nature reserve.

Reserve management

Initially, when excavation ceased in the new reserve area, the pit was carefully profiled to create a variety of lakes, lagoons, ponds and islands. Subsequent management (see Table 7.1) has been aimed at producing ideal nesting cover for breeding ducks and feeding and loafing areas for wintering wildfowl. This work has resulted in a rich wetland, with a mixed vegetation structure which is extremely attractive to a variety of wildlife. The area now holds many more species than did the semi-open improved grassland which existed in the flood plain of the river Great Ouse when extraction began in the 1940s. The end result of gravel extraction at Great Linford has, therefore, been a large increase in the diversity and abundance of wildlife within the area managed for conservation.

Aquatic vegetation

Since 1972, the emphasis in management of the reserve has changed as the habitat has matured. At first, much effort was expended in planting the bare shores of the lakes and the interior of the reserve. Emergent aquatic plants were introduced to water margins to speed up the process of colonisation and to reduce problems with erosion. There was a high success rate in establishing most plants and these - and self-colonists - spread rapidly, especially in the shallow lagoons in the St Peter's area. One interesting early independent arrival was sea club-rush, a plant of brackish waters, which proved a vigorous coloniser. It was more difficult to establish common reed. This plant prefers to be planted in damp, rather than wet ground, and it then spreads towards and into the water. The difficulty was overcome when lake levels in the reserve were reduced and now several small reed beds are gradually expanding. All the lagoons and lakes have well vegetated edges. The diversity of species of emergent plants provides a variety of food and shelter, supporting a range of wildlife. Chapter 1 details recommended species of plants for reserve development.

Submerged aquatic plants were mainly independent colonisers, but their establishment in Main Lake was severely restricted by the actions of a high density of coarse fish. Successful germination and growth from the existing seedbank followed the removal of fish in November 1987 (Wright & Phillips, 1992).

Table 7.1 Annual cycle of reserve management in the Great Linford Reserve.

Annual tasks	J	F	M	A	M	J	J	A	S	O	N	D
Mow paths					*	*	*	*	*			
Mow wildflower meadow & remove 'hay'							*	*				
Graze grass paddocks (c.2 sheep/ha)		*	*						*	*		
Graze wildfowl loafing banks				*	*	*	*	*				
Coppice osier bed (5yr. rotation in strips)	*										*	*
Coppice willow/alder on islands. ★	*										*	*
Coppice willow/alder on mainland ★	*										*	*
Manipulate water levels: i) lower for wading birds					*	*		*	*	*		
ii) raise for nesting waterfowl		*	*	*	*							
Spray with approved herbicide to reduce invasive emergent aquatic growth					*	*	*	*	*			

(★ · Coppicing is rotational and a few willow & alder are maintained as standards).

The spined loach is a threatened species but it lives in the lakes of the ARC Wildfowl Reserve.

An aerial view of the varied habitats of the St Peter's lagoons.

Planting lake margins can assist plant coloniation in the early years.

Sea club rush arrived on its own . . . *Phragmites* was introduced by planting.

Table 7.2 Aquatic vegetation in the Great Linford Wildfowl Reserve.

Emergent

Water horsetail	*Equisetum fluviatile*
Marsh horsetail	*Equisetum palustre*
Common Reed	*Phragmites australis*
Reed sweet grass	*Glyceria maxima*
Great pond sedge	*Carex riparia*
Lesser pond sedge	*Carex acutiformis*
Hairy sedge	*Carex hirta*
Glaucous sedge	*Carex flacca*
False fox-sedge	*Carex obtrubae*
Tufted sedge	*Carex paniculata*
Common spike rush	*Eleocharis palustris*
Bulrush	*Scirpus (Schoenoplectus) lacustris*
Sea club rush	*Scirpus maritimus*
Hard rush	*Juncus inflexus*
Soft rush	*Juncus effusus*
Jointed rush	*Juncus articulatus*
Round-headed rush	*Juncus compressus*
Flowering rush	*Butomus umbellatus*
Water plantain	*Alisma plantago-aquatica*
Greater reedmace	*Typha latifolia*
Lesser reedmace	*Typha augustifolia*
Yellow flag	*Iris pseudacorus*
Branched bur-reed	*Sparganium erectum*
Unbranched bur-reed	*Sparganium emersum*
Trifid bur-marigold	*Bidens tripartita*
Amphibious bistort	*Polygonum amphibium*
Great water dock	*Rumex hydrolapathum*
Fools watercress	*Apium nodiflorum*
Water parsnip	*Berula erecta*
Watercress	*Nasturtium officinale*
Great yellow-cress	*Rorippa amphibia*
Marsh yellow-cress	*Rorippa palustris*
Gipsywort	*Lycopus europaeus*
Brooklime	*Veronica beccabunga*
Water speedwell	*Veronica anagallis aquatica*
Pink water speedwell	*Veronica catenata*
Water figwort	*Scrophularia auriculata*
Water forget-me-not	*Myosotis scorpioides*
Water mint	*Mentha aquatica*
Arrowhead	*Sagittaria sagittifolia*

Submerged/floating

Broad-leaved pondweed	*Potamogeton natans*
Fennel-leaved pondweed	*Potamogeton pectinatus*
Perfoliate pondweed	*Potamogeton perfoliatus*
Curled pondweed	*Potamogeton crispus*
Small pondweed	*Potamogeton berchtoldii*
Lesser pondweed	*Potamogeton pusillus*
Canadian pondweed	*Elodea canadensis*
Horned pondweed	*Zannichelia palustris*
Common duckweed	*Lemna minor*
Ivy-leaved duckweed	*Lemna trisulca*
Water crowfoot	*Ranunculus aquatica*
Fan-leaved water crowfoot	*Ranunculus circinatus*
Common startwort	*Callitriche stagnalis*
Blunt-fruited starwort	*Callitriche obtusangula Callitriche hermaphroditica*
Spiked water milfoil	*Myriophyllum spicatum*
White water-lily	*Nymphaea alba*
Yellow water-lily	*Nuphar lutea*
Fringed water-lily	*Nymphoides peltata*

Sampling submerged plants and aquatic invertebrates in St Peter's lake

Terrestrial vegetation

On land, the reserve has been managed as a mosaic of grassland, willow and alder scrub with a variety of other shrubs and trees (Table 7.4). County Councils often have approved planting lists - some specific to areas of a county. These lists can be used, together with the experience of the ecologists involved, to produce ideal schemes for given sites. In structure, the vegetation grades up gradually from the emergent plants in the water's edge, through low woody scrub to taller trees. A range of different vegetation heights is encouraged by mowing and coppicing

Fringed water lily: Attractive and beneficial.

selected areas. Coppicing is a traditional system in which trees are periodically cut back to ground level to encourage bushy regrowth. Willow and alder are the main species coppiced; an osier bed is maintained in three strips which are coppiced in a 5-year rotation. Open grassland is maintained by mowing and/or grazing. Goats have been used in the reserve to reduce woody growth, especially on islands. They are effective browsers but they need careful husbandry and regular handling or they become unmanageable and often escape to damage areas where they are not wanted. Sheep grazing in early spring and autumn maintains a good grass sward and primitive breeds such as the Soay or Hebridean are also effective browsers. Sheep need less shelter and, if trained to feed from a bucket, are easier to manage than goats. All livestock should be checked daily.

Control of excessive vegetation

In recent years, the amount of selective tree removal and coppicing has been increased to prevent the reserve from becoming too densely wooded. Where regrowth is undesirable, cut stumps are treated with a mixture of diesel and Garlon (ICI Agrochemicals).

Similarly, some spraying and mechanical removal of aquatic plants has become necessary to prevent shallow water from infilling and drying out (Table 7.3). Physical removal by hand is only practical in small areas. Alternatively, anchored black polythene sheeting is a cheap and effective method of clearing weeds without detriment to other wildlife. After four to six weeks in place in early summer, aquatic vegetation is shaded out and killed, leaving a clear patch. Several sheets used in this way can create a mosaic of open water and weed beds. Machines such as hydraulic excavators are necessary for large-scale weed clearance. Experience at Great Linford suggests that channels and ponds 0.5-2m deep become shallow and choked after 15-20 years and require remedial action unless the natural succession is to be allowed to proceed. When such areas are cleared, work is undertaken in autumn/winter and the out-take is removed well away from the water's edge. Clearing can take place in the growing season but vegetation must not be left to rot on the banks as run-off will cause nutrient enrichment and possible de-oxygenation in the water. Water plants transplant readily and when clearing work is proposed it is useful to offer plant material for use in new sites locally.

Mechanical methods of control cause drastic disturbance to invertebrates and untouched patches should be left to allow re-colonisation. Chemical control is less destructive in this way as the animals leave their host

plant as it dies. The residual dead plant material, however, may still have to be removed to avoid accumulation of organic matter and possible de-oxygenation problems. It is better to use herbicides to treat small blocks rather than large areas at any one time. The use of approved herbicides to control aquatic vegetation can be effective, simple and safe, providing the manufacturers' instructions are carefully followed. 'Guidelines For The Use Of Herbicides In Or Near Water' (MAFF Bulletin B2078) should be consulted and the correct herbicide selected for the given problem (Table 7.3). Timing herbicide use is important; usually, the more active the weed growth, the better the uptake of the herbicide and the resulting level of control. Early use reduces the amount of plant material rotting down in the water.

Algae can often present particularly difficult problems, especially where eutrophication is occurring. In

Table 7.3 Chemical control of vegetation in and around water.

Problem	Herbicide
Emergent broad-leaved plants: eg:Reedmace, Bur-reeds.	Glyphosates: Roundup (Monsanto Ltd) Spasor (May & Baker)
except: Marestail *(Hippuris vulgaris)* Arrowhead	Dichlobenil: Casoron -G or Casoron-GSR (ICIAgrochemicals)
Emergent narrow-leaved plants eg:Sweet Reedgrass	Dalapon (Dow Chemicals Ltd)
Floating-leaved plants: eg:Waterlilies, Amphibious Bistort, Duckweeds, Blanketweed	Chlorthiamid: 'Prefix' Diquat: Reglone or Midstream (ICI Agrochemicals) Terbutryne: Clarosan (Ciba Geigy)
except: Broad-leaved pondweed (*Potamogeton natans*)	partial susceptibility to Diquat and Terbutryne. Repeat treatments.
Submerged plants: eg:Hornworts, milfoils, Canadian Pondweed	Chlorthiamid Diquat Terbutryne Dichlobenil
Algae	Diquat Terbutryne
(including unicellular, filamentous & blue/green	Barley straw *(see text)*

nutrient-rich waters, algae can increase rapidly to form a covering layer which prevents light penetration and can cause oxygen depletion. It should be noted that algal blooms can be caused by unbalancing the system through over zealous removal of the higher aquatic plants. A benign and effective alternative to physical removal or herbicide treatment was discovered by

Table 7.4 Trees and shrubs in the Great Linford Reserve. Species marked * are not native or are unsuitable for the area and would not now be planted.

Tall outer zone trees and scattered standards · provide shelter and nest sites (especially holes and splits for tits, owls and bats); harbour a wide invertebrate fauna in both living and dead wood. Flowers of willows provide an early source of nectar and pollen.

Crack willow	*Salix fragilis*
Grey willow	*Salix cinerea*
White willow	*Salix alba*
Common oak	*Quercus robur*
Ash	*Fraxinus excelsior*
Wych elm	*Ulmus glabra*
English elm	*Ulmus procera*
Hornbeam	*Carpinus betulus*
*Grey poplar	*Populus canescens*
*Scots pine	*Pinus sylvestris*
*Horse chestnut	*Aesculus hippocastanum*

Small trees and shrubs · provide shelter and some nest sites; harbour a good invertebrate fauna; flowers attract nectar feeders; berries/fruits are important winter food for some birds and small mammals.

Field maple	*Acer campestre*
Alder	*Alnus glutinosa*
*Grey alder	*Alnus incana*
Silver birch	*Betula pendula*
Hazel	*Corylus avellana*
Hawthorn	*Crataegus monogyna*
Alder buckthorn	*Frangula alnus*
Apple	*Malvus domestica*
Wild cherry	*Prunus avium*
Crab apple	*Malvus sylvestris*
Blackthorn	*Prunus spinosa*
Buckthorn	*Rhamnus catharticus*
Goat willow	*Salix caprea*
Osier	*Salix viminalis*
Spindle	*Euonymus europaeus*
Rowan	*Sorbus aucuparia*
Aspen	*Populus tremula*
Holly	*Ilex aquifolium*
Elder	*Sambucus nigra*

Low shrubs · provide thick cover from 0-1.5m utilised by nesting ducks (especially bramble) and songbirds; varied invertebrate fauna and berries/fruits.

Wild privet	*Ligustrum vulgare*
Wayfaring tree	*Viburnum lantana*
Common gorse	*Ulex europaeus*
Dog rose	*Rosa canina*
Bramble	*Rubus fructiosus*
Dogwood	*Cornus sanguinea*
Guelder rose	*Viburnum opulatus*
*Japanese honeysuckle	*Lonicera nitida*

Table 7.5 Species list of the higher plants recorded in the Great Linford reserve since 1972, excluding aquatic species and trees and shrubs listed in Tables 7.2 & 7.4.

Horsetails and grasses

Common horsetail	*Equisetum arvense*
Reed grass	*Phalaris arundinacea*
Barren fescue	*Vulpia bromoides*
Canary grass	*Phalaris canariensis*
Couch grass	*Agropyron repens*
Rats tail fescue	*Vulpia myuros*
Perennial rye grass	*Lolium perenne*
Timothy grass	*Phleum pratense*
Meadow foxtail	*Alopecurus pratensis*
Annual meadow grass	*Poa annua*
Cocks foot	*Dactylis glomerata*
Tufted hair grass	*Deschampsia caespitosa*
Wavy hair grass	*Deschampsia flexuosa*
Meadow barley	*Hordeum secalinum*
Wall barley	*Hordeum murinum*
Wild oat	*Avena fatua*
Common bent	*Agrostis tenuis*
Fine bent	*Agrostis stolonifera*
Yorkshire fog	*Holcus lanatus*
Crested dogs tail	*Cynosurus cristatus*
Black grass	*Alopecurus myosuroides*
Smooth meadow grass	*Poa pratensis*
Rough meadow grass	*Poa trivialis*
Lop grass	*Bromus mollis*
Black bent	*Agrostis gigantea*
Hairy oat	*Heliototrichon pubescens*
Oat grass	*Arrhenatherum elatius*
Marsh foxtail	*Alopecurus geniculatus*
Cats-tail	*Phleum bertolonii*
Lords and ladies	*Arum maculatum*
Black bryony	*Tamus communis*

St John's-worts

Perforate St Johns-wort	*Hypericum perforatus*

Plantains

Hoary plantain	*Plantago media*
Rat-tail plantain	*Plantago major*
Ribwort plantain	*Plantago lanceolata*

Daisy family

Coltsfoot	*Tussilago farfara*
Groundsel	*Senecio vulgaris*
Sticky groundsel	*Senecio viscosus*
Oxford ragwort	*S. squlidus*
Hoary ragwort	*S. erucifolius*
Ragwort	*S. jacobea*
Dandelion	*Taraxacum officinale*
Daisy	*Bellis perennis*
Yarrow	*Achillea millefolium*
Beaked hawksbeard	*Crepis vesicaria*
Smooth hawksbeard	*Crepis capillaris*
Ox-eye daisy	*Chrysanthemum leucanthemum*
Musk thistle	*Carduus nutans*
Spear thistle	*Cirsium vulgare*
Meadow thistle	*C. arvense*
Hardhead	*Centaurea nigra*
Salsify	*Tragopogon porrifolius*
Goatsbeard	*T. pratensis*
Trifid bur-marigold	*Bidens tripartita*
Marsh cudweed	*Gnaphalium uliginosum*
Mugwort	*Atremesia vulgaris*
Scentless mayweed	*Tripleurospermum inodora*
Wild chamomile	*Matricaria recutita*
Pineapple weed	*Matricaria matricarioides*
Autumn hawksbit	*Leontodon autumnalis*
Prickly ox-tongue	*Picris echioides*
Prickly sow thistle	*Sonchus asper*
Perennial sow thistle	*Sonchus arvensis*
Stinking mayweed	*Anthemis cotula*
Burdock	*Arctium minus*

Tansy	*Tanacetum vulgare*
Nipplewort	*Lapsana communis*
Wild lettuce	*Lactuca virosa*
Prickly lettuce	*Lactuca serriola*
Hemp agrimony	*Eupatorium cannabinum*

Dock family

Redleg	*Polygonum persica*
Knotgrass	*P. aviculare*
Black bindweed	*P. convolvulus*
Sharp dock	*Rumex conglomeratus*
Broad-leaved dock	*R. obtusifolium*
Sorrel	*R. acetosa*
Curled dock	*R. crispus*
Red-veined dock	*R. sanguineus*

Willowherbs

Square-stemmed willowherb	*Epilobium adriatum*
Marsh willowherb	*E. palustre*
Great willowherb	*E. hirsutum*
Hoary willowherb	*E. parviflorum*
Rosebay willowherb	*Chaemaenerion angustifolium*

Nettles

Pellitory of the wall	*Parietaria repens*
Stinging nettle	*Urtica dioica*

Buttercup family

Creeping buttercup	*Ranunculus repens*
Bulbous buttercup	*R. bulbosus*
Lesser celandine	*R. ficaria*
Meadow buttercup	*R. acris*
Celery-leaved buttercup	*R. scleratus*

Carrot family

Cow parsley	*Anthriscus sylvatica*
Wild carrot	*Daucus carota*
Hogweed	*Heracleum sphondylium*
Hemlock	*Conium maculatum*
Pignut	*Conopodium majus*
Upright hedge parsley	*Torilis japonica*
Wild angelica	*Angelica sylvestris*
Ground elder	*Aegopodium podagraria*

Spurges

Sun spurge	*Euphorbia helioscopa*
Dwarf spurge	*E. enigma*

Bindweeds

Field convolvulus	*Convolvulus arvensis*
Great bindweed	*Calystegia sepium*

Loosestrifes

Purple loosestrife	*Lythrum salicaria*

Sonecrops

Biting stonecrop	*Sedum acre*

Goosefoots

Fat hen	*Chenopodium album*
Goosefoot	*Atriplex patula*
Red goosefoot	*Chenopodium rubrum*
Spear-leaved orache	*Atriplex hastata*

Cabbage family

Garlic mustard	*Alliaria petiolata*
Hedge mustard	*Sisymbrium officinale*
Hairy bittercress	*Cardamine hirsuta*
Common whitlow grass	*Erphila verna*
Lady's smock	*Cardamine pratensis*
Charlock	*Sinapsis arvensis*
Wild radish	*Raphanus raphanistrum*
Field penny cress	*Thalapsis arvensis*
Shepherd's purse	*Capsella bursa-pastoris*
Winter cress	*Barbarea vulgaris*

Pea family

Black medic	*Medicago lupulina*
Tufted vetch	*Vicia cracca*
Common vetch	*V. sativa*
Bush vetch	*V. sepium*
Birds foot trefoil	*Lotus corniculatus*
Marsh birds foot trefoil	*L. uliginosum*
Meadow pea	*Lathyrus pratensis*
Grass vetchling	*L. nissolia*

Red clover	*Trifolium pratense*
White clover	*T. repens*

Labiate family

Common hemp-nettle	*Galeopsis tetrahit*
Self heal	*Prunella vulgaris*
Hedge woundwort	*Stachys sylvatica*
Marsh woundwort	*S. palustris*
Water mint	*Mentha aquatica*
White dead-nettle	*Lamium album*
Red dead-nettle	*L. purpurea*
Ground Ivy	*Glechoma hederacea*
Skullcap	*Scutellaria galericulata*

Pink family

Thyme-leaved sandwort	*Arenaria serpyfolia*
Common mouse-ear chickweed	*Cerastium fontanum*
Sticky mouse-ear chickweed	*C. glomeratum*
Common chickweed	*Stellaria media*
Red campion	*Silene dioica*
White campion	*S. alba*
Corn spurry	*Spergula arvensis*
Annual pearlwort	*Sagina apetala*

Rose family

Meadowsweet	*Filipendula ulmaria*
Creeping cinquefoil	*Potentilla reptans*
Silverweed	*P. anserina*
Blackberry	*Rubus fructiosus agg.*
Dog rose	*Rosa canina*

Figwort family

Common field speedwell	*Veronica persica*
Wall speedwell	*V. cataneta*
Germander speedwell	*V. chamaedrys*
Marsh speedwell	*V. scutellata*
Thyme-leaved speedwell	*V. serpyllifolia*
Foxglove	*Digitalis purpurea*
Red bartsia	*Bartsia odonites*
Yellow rattle	*Rhinanthus minor*

Borage family

Comfrey	*Symphytum officinale*
Field forget-me-not	*Myosotis arvensis*
Wood foret-me-not	*M. sylvatica*
Borage	*Borago officinalis*

Bedstraws

Lady's bedstraw	*Galium verum*
Goosegrass	*G. aparine*

Primrose family

Cowslip	*Primula veris*
Scarlet pimpernel	*Anagallis arvensis*

Valerian family

Common valerian	*Valeriana officinalis*

Teasel family

Teasel	*Dipsacus fullonum*

Nightshades

Woody nightshade	*Solanum dulcamara*
Black nightshade	*S. nigra*

Ivy family

Ivy	*Hedera helix*

Cranesbills

Small flowered cranesbill	*Geranium pusillum*
Cut-leaved cranesbill	*G. dissectum*
Meadow cranesbill	*G. pratense*
Shining cranesbill	*G. lucidum*
Dovesfoot cranesbill	*G. molle*

Balsams

Orange balsam	*Impatiens capensis*

Mallow family

Common mallow	*Malva sylvestris*
Musk mallow	*M. moschata*
Dwarf mallow	*M. neglecta*

Orchid family

Common spotted orchid	*Dactylorchis fuschii*
Bee orchid	*Ophrys apifera*

accident at Great Linford and simultaneously by Dr Pip Barrett at the Aquatic Weeds Research Unit, Sonning, Berks. At Great Linford barley straw was added to new water bodies to provide a substrate and nutrients for invertebrate colonisation (Street & Titmus 1982). During the experiments clear water, free of algae, was noted in the vicinity of the decomposing straw. Further investigations have confirmed a strong algistatic effect of rotting straw and straw treatment has since been used effectively in both still and flowing waters. Recommended dosage is about one to two bales per acre.

Reserve monitoring

As a result of habitat management, the reserve at Great Linford has a much greater species diversity than comparable areas elsewhere on the site. Since 1972, records have been kept of the flora and fauna by the staff of the Wildfowl Centre and also by local naturalists. Birds and dragonflies have been particularly well recorded and are dealt with in detail below. They serve as examples of the many groups which thrive in this artificial wetland.

Flora

After 20 years development, the flora in the reserve has stabilised; new species are found less than annually. The most notable species is round-fruited rush (*Juncus compressus*), a scarce plant of damp ground. Table 7.5 is a complete species list of plants in the reserve.

Invertebrates

The mosaic of wetland, grassland, scrub and taller trees supports a diverse invertebrate fauna. Not all groups have received attention yet, but 68 species of moths have been recorded - mainly during a period of trapping in 1979. The habitat has diversified since then and more species could now be expected. Twenty-four species of butterfly have been recorded and there is a notable assemblage of dragonflies. The reserve now fulfils the requirements for SSSI status for its community of breeding dragonfly species alone.

All dragonflies must have freshwater in which to breed. The presence of a good variety of species of breeding dragonflies in a watercourse or wetland can be taken as an indication of good water quality.

Dragonfly larvae are predators of other benthic invertebrates, fish-fry and tadpoles. The larval stage can be completed within a year or may take several years.

Table 7.6 Lepidoptera (moths)

Ghost	*Hepialus humuli humuli*
Common swift	*Hepialus lupulinus*
Six-spot burnet	*Zygaena filipendulae*
Buff arches	*Habrosyne pyritoides*
Figure of eight	*Tethea ocularis octogesimea*
Single-dotted wave	*Idaea dimidiata*
Riband wave	*Idaea aversata*
Shaded broad-bar	*Scotopteryx chenopodiata*
Barred straw	*Eulithis pyraliata*
Common marbled carpet	*Hydriomena furcata*
Swallow-tailed moth	*Ourapteryx sambucaria*
Peppered moth	*Biston betularia*
Mottled beauty	*Alcis repandata repandata*
Common white wave	*Cabera pusaria*
Common wave	*Cabera exanthemata*
Eyed hawk	*Smerinthus ocellata*
Poplar hawk	*Laothoe populi*
Elephant hawk	*Deilephila elpenor*
Buff-tip	*Phalera bucephala*
Sallow kitten	*Furcula furcula*
Swallow prominent	*Phoesia tremula*
Pale prominent	*Pterostoma palpina*
White satin	*Leucoma salicis*
Garden tiber	*Arctia caja*
White ermine	*Spilosoma lubricipeda*
Buff erine	*Spilosoma luteum*
Cinnabar	*Tyria jacobaeae*
Turnip moth	*Agrotis segetum*
Heart and dart	*Agrotis exclamationis*
Flame	*Axylia putris*
Flame shoulder	*Ochropleura plecta*
Small square-spot	*Diarsia rubi*
Gothic	*Naenia typica*
Nutmeg	*Discestra trifolii*
Cabbage moth	*Mamestra brassicae*
Dot moth	*Melanchra persicariae*
Pale-shouldered brocade	*Lacanobia thalassina*
Varied coronet	*Hadena compta*
Lychnis	*Hadena bicruris*
Smoky wainscot	*Mythimna impura impura*
Common wainscot	*Mythimna pallens*
Sycamore	*Acronicta aceris*
Grey dagger	*Acronicta psi*
Brown rustic	*Rusina ferruginea*
Small angle shades	*Euplexia lucipara*
Dingy shears	*Enargia ypsillon*
Dark arches	*Apamea monoglypha*
Light arches	*Apamea lithoxylaea*
Cloud-bordered brindle	*Apamea crenata*
Clouded brindle	*Apamea epomidion*
Dusky brocade	*Apamea remissa*
Small clouded brindle	*Apamea unanimis*
Rustic shoulder-knot	*Apamea sordens*
Marbled minor	*Oligia strigilis*
Tawny marbled minor	*Oligia latruncula*
Middle-barred minor	*Oligia fasciuncula*
Common rustic	*Mesapamea secalis*
Small dotted buff	*Photedes minima*
Uncertain	*Hoplodrina alcines*
Rustic	*Hoplodrina blanda*
Mottled rustic	*Caradrina morpheus*
Red Underwing	*Catocala nupta*
Burnished brass	*Diachrysia chrysitis*
Silver Y	*Autographa gamma*
Plain golden Y	*Autographa jota*
Spectacle	*Abrostola triplasia*
Snout	*Hypena proboscidalis*

Table 7.7 Lepidoptera (butterflies) * denotes breeding.

Clouded yellow	*Colias croceus* (migrant)
Brimstone	*Gonoteryx rhamni**
Large white	*Pieris brassicae*
Small white	*Pieris rapae**
Green-veined white	*Pieris napi**
Orange tip	*Anthocharis cardamines**
Black hairstreak	*Satyrium pruni* (one 1985)
Small copper	*Lycaena phlaeas**
Common blue	*Polyommatus icarus**
Holly blue	*Celastrina argiolus**
Red admiral	*Vanessa atalanta**
Painted lady	*Cynthia cardui* (migrant)
Small tortoiseshell	*Aglais uticae**
Peacock	*Elnachis io**
Comma	*Polygonia c-album**
Marbled white	*Melanargia galathea*
Speckled wood	*Parage aegeria*
Wall	*Lasiommata megera**
Gatekeeper	*Pyronia tithonus**
Meadow brown	*Maniola jurtina**
Ringlet	*Aphantopus hyperantus**
Small heath	*Coenonympha pamphilus**
Small skipper	*Thymelicus flavus**
Large skipper	*Ochlodes venatus**

Table 7.8. Odonata (dragonflies and damselflies) *denotes breeding.

White-legged damselfly	*Platycnemis pennipes**
Red-eyed damselfly	*Erythroma najas**
Azure damselfly	*Coenagrion puella**
Common blue damselfly	*Enallagma cyathigerum**
Large red damselfly	*Pyrrhosoma nyphula**
Blue-tailed damselfly	*Ishnura elegans**
Banded demoiselle	*Calopteryx splendens**
Southern hawker	*Aeshna cyanea*
Brown hawker	*Aeshna grandis**
Migrant hawker	*Aeshna mixta**
Emperor dragonfly	*Anax imperator*
Black-tailed skimmer	*Orthetrum cancellatum**
Broad-bodied chaser	*Libellula depressa**
Four-spotted chaser	*Libellula quadrimaculata**
Ruddy darter	*Sympetrum sangineum**
Common darter	*Sympetrum striolatum**

Adults too are predators, catching other insects on the wing. They may be found considerable distances from water but they must return to it to mate and to lay eggs.

As gravel pits mature and accumulate organic debris, which aquatic invertebrates colonise, they often become attractive to dragonflies. At Great Linford, extensive shallow water with few fish predators and abundant submerged and emergent vegetation, provides good shelter and foraging for larvae and sites for larvae to emerge when changing to adults. The tall herb-rich grassland attracts numerous flying insects and is a rich hunting area for adult dragonflies, whilst the shrubs provide shelter. Sixteen species have been recorded in the reserve and another has been seen elsewhere on the site.

Of the larger dragonflies, brown hawker, four-spotted chaser, black-tailed skimmer, common and ruddy darter all breed in good numbers. Black-tailed skimmer is an early coloniser of new waters as it favours bare ground to hunt over. In contrast, ruddy darter is a recent arrival as it requires densely vegetated, marshy ground. Some overgrown pools now suit it. Broad-bodied chaser also breeds in the reserve, though not annually. In some years migrant hawkers are seen ovipositing. Migrant hawkers arrive each autumn in variable numbers; there was a spectacular invasion in 1991. Southern hawker has yet to be recorded breeding.

Azure, red-eyed, banded, blue-tailed and common blue damselflies all breed in the reserve. Banded damselfly are even more numerous on the River Ouse alongside the reserve boundary. The river also supports breeding white-legged damselfly, an uncommon species. The proximity of the reserve is likely to be important to

Banded Demoiselle. Sixteen species of *Odonata* have been recorded at Great Linford.

this species, which feeds over areas managed for tall grasses and flowers such as umbellifers (eg upright hedge parsley) which attract numerous insects.

The large red damselfly has been seen in the reserve and emerald damselfly recorded on the site, though not yet in the reserve.

The reserve, therefore, has a notable assemblage of dragonflies and the presence of ruddy darter and white-legged damselfly make it locally important.

Fish

A wide range of species of fish have been found, including spined loach, which is uncommon both nationally and on a European level. The reserve lakes have never been stocked but winter flooding gives fish in the River Great Ouse access to the lakes.

Table 7.9 Fish

Pike	*Esox lucius*
Carp	*Cyprinus carpio*
Roach	*Rutilus rutilus*
Rudd	*Scardinius erythropthalmus*
Minnow	*Phoxinus phoxinus*
Tench	*Tinca tinca*
Gudgeon	*Gobio gobio*
Dace	*Leuciscus leuciscus*
Bleak	*Alburnus alburnus*
Silver Bream	*Blicca bjoerkna*
Common Bream	*Abramis brama*
Stone Loach	*Neomachilus barbatulus*
Spined Loach	*Cobitis taenia*
Eel	*Anguilla anguilla*
Perch	*Perca fluvitilis*
Ruffe	*Gymnocephalus cernua*
Bullhead	*Cottus gobio*
Three-spined stickleback	*Gasterosteus aculeatus*
Ten-spined stickleback	*Pungitius pungitius*
Zander	*Stizostedion lucioperca*

Amphibians and reptiles

The rare great crested newt (which has full protection under the terms of the Wildlife and Countryside Act 1981) has been found in at least one pond in the reserve. Natural colonisation of new waters by amphibians is relatively slow and at Great Linford some toad and frog spawn was introduced from local ponds. An increase in numbers of amphibians, particularly common frogs, has been recorded in recent years. Grass snakes are also frequently seen, reflecting their prevalence in this area.

Table 7.10 Amphibians

Smooth newt	*Triturus vulgaris*
Great crested newt	*Triturus cristatus*
Common toad	*Bufo bufo*
Common frog	*Rana temporaria*
Reptiles	
Grass snake	*Natrix natrix*
Slow worm	*Anguis fragilis*

Birds

Between 1972 and the end of 1991, 189 bird species had been recorded at Great Linford. Most occurred in the reserve area and 70 species have been recorded breeding at least once. Table 7.11 is a complete list of birds seen in the reserve since 1972, excluding wildfowl and waders which are listed in Chapters 3 and 4. A few species have declined or ceased to breed since extraction finished. For example, sand martins nested in temporary sand cliffs and formed huge roosts in the silt settling beds. They are still recorded on passage but an artificial cliff incoporated into the Main Lake bund in 1989 has not yet attracted nesting pairs.

Table 7.11 A list of species of bird seen in the reserve 1972 - 1991, excluding ducks, geese, swans and waders.
* - denotes breeding; ⌐ – rare (< 10 records)

Grebes
Little grebe	*Tachybaptus ruficollis**
Great crested grebe	*Podiceps cristatus**
Red-necked grebe	*Podiceps grisegena⌐*
Slavonian grebe	*Podiceps auritus⌐*
Black-necked grebe	*Podiceps nigricollis*

Shearwaters
Manx shearwater	*Puffinus puffinus⌐*

Cormorants
Cormorant	*Phalacrocorax carbo*
Shag	*Phalacrocorax aristotelis*

Herons and bitterns
Bittern	*Botaurus stellaris*
Grey heron	*Ardea cinerea*

Raptors
Osprey	*Pandion haliaetus*
Buzzard	*Buteo buteo⌐*
Marsh harrier	*Circus aeruginosus⌐*
Montagu's harrier	*Circus pygargus⌐*
Goshawk	*Accipiter gentilis⌐*
Sparrowhawk	*Accipiter nisus*
Kestrel	*Falco tinnunculus**
Merlin	*Faco columbarius*
Hobby	*Falco subbuteo*

Gamebirds
Red-legged partridge	*Alectoris rufa**
Grey partridge	*Perdix perdix**
Quail	*Coturnix coturnix⌐*
Pheasant	*Phasianus colchicus**

Rails and crakes
Water rail	*Rallus aquaticus**
Moorhen	*Gallinula chloropus**
Coot	*Fulica atra**

Gulls and terns
Little gull	*Larus minutus*
Black-headed gull	*Larus ridibundus*
Lesser black-backed gull	*Larus fuscus*
Herring gull	*Larus argentatus*
Greater black-backed gull	*Larus marinus*
Common gull	*Larus canus*
Black tern	*Childonias niger*
Sandwich tern	*Sterna sandvicensis⌐*
Common tern	*Sterna hirundo**
Arctic tern	*Sterna paradisaea*
Little tern	*Sterna albifrons⌐*

Pigeons and doves
Woodpigeon	*Columba palumbus**
Stock dove	*Columba oenas**
Collared dove	*Streptopelia decaocto*
Turtle dove	*Streptopelia turtur**

Cuckoos
Cuckoo	*Cuculus canorus**

Owls
Barn owl	*Tyto alba*
Long-eared owl	*Asio otus*
Short-eared owl	*Asio flammeus*
Little owl	*Athene noctua**
Tawny owl	*Strix aluco*

Swifts
Swift	*Apus apus*

Kingfishers
Kingfisher	*Alcedo atthis**

Woodpeckers
Green woodpecker	*Picus viridis**
Great spotted woodpecker	*Dendrocopus major**
Lesser spotted woodpecker	*Dendrocopus minor**

Larks
Skylark	*Alauda arvensis**

Swallows and martins
Sand martin	*Riparia riparia**
Swallow	*Hirundo rustica**
House martin	*Delichon urbica*

Pipits and wagtails
Tree pipit	*Anthus trivialis*
Meadow pipit	*Anthus pratensis*
Water pipit	*Anthus spinoletta*
Yellow wagtail	*Montacilla flava**
Grey wagtail	*Montacilla cinerea*
Pied wagtail	*Montacilla alba**

Shrikes
Great grey shrike	*Lanius excubitor*

Wrens
Wren	*Troglodytes troglodytes**

Accentors
Dunnock	*Prunella modularis**

Warblers, flycatchers, thrushes etc.
Grasshopper warbler	*Locustlla naevia**
Sedge warbler	*Acrocephalus schoenobaenus**
Marsh warbler	*Acrocephalus palustris⌐*
Reed warbler	*Acrocephalus scirpaceus**
Garden warbler	*Sylvia borin**
Blackcap	*Sylvia atricapilla**
Whitethroat	*Sylvia communis**
Lesser whitethroat	*Sylvia curruca**
Willow warbler	*Phylloscopus trochilus**
Chiffchaff	*Phylloscopus collybita*
Wood warbler	*Phylloscopus sibilatrix⌐*
Goldcrest	*Regulus regulus*
Pied flycatcher	*Ficedula hypoleuca*
Spotted flycatcher	*Muscicapa striata*
Whinchat	*Saxicola rubetra*
Stonechat	*Saxicola torquata*
Wheatear	*Oenanthe oenanthe*
Redstart	*Phoenicurus phoenicurus (*1977)*
Robin	*Erithacus rubecula**
Nightingale	*Luscinia megarhynchos⌐*
Bluethroat	*Luscinia svecico⌐*
Fieldfare	*Turdus pilaris*
Ring ouzel	*Turdus torquatus⌐*
Blackbird	*Turdus merula**
Redwing	*Turdus iliacus*
Song thrush	*Turdus philomelos**
Mistle thrush	*Turdus viscivorus**

Tits
Long-tailed tit	*Aegithalos caudatus**
Marsh tit	*Parus palustris⌐*
Willow tit	*Parus montanus⌐*
Coal tit	*Parus ater*
Blue tit	*Parus caeruleus**
Great tit	*Parus major**

Nuthatches
Nuthatch	*Sitta europaea*

Treecreepers
Treecreeper	*Certhia familiaris*

Buntings
Corn bunting	*Emberiza calandra*
Yellowhammer	*Emberiza citrinella**
Reed bunting	*Emberiza schoeniclus**

Finches
Chaffinch	*Fringilla coelebs**
Brambling	*Fringilla montifringilla*
Greenfinch	*Carduelis chloris**
Siskin	*Carduelis spinus*
Goldfinch	*Carduelis carduelis**
Linnet	*Acanthis cannabina**
Redpoll	*Acanthis flammea*
Crossbill	*Loxia curvirostra*
Bullfinch	*Pyrrhula pyrrhula**
Hawfinch	*Coccothraustes coccothraustes⌐*

Sparrows
House sparrow	*Passer domesticus**
Tree sparrow	*Passer montanus**

Starlings
Starling	*Sturnus vulgaris**

Crows
Jay	*Garrulus glandarius*
Magpie	*Pica pica**
Jackdaw	*Corvus monedula**
Rook	*Corvus frugilegus*
Carrion crow	*Corvus corone corone**
Raven	*Corvus corax⌐*

Breeding birds

Breeding waterfowl have been regularly monitored at Great Linford since 1972. In 1990 the first annual Common Bird Census (CBC) was carried out to assess the value of the reserve to birds other than waterfowl. Also in 1990, using the CBC method, the bird community of the reserve was compared with that of other parts of the site, where there was no habitat management (Phillips & Phillips, 1991). The CBC method has been developed by the British Trust for Ornithology over the last 20 years and is widely accepted as the most accurate and practical way to count the breeding birds of a particular area. It works well in a variety of habitats and takes account of the variations in behaviour and conspicuousness of different species.

During CBC visits, 65 species were seen in 1990 in the reserve and 68 species in 1991. These totals include waterbirds, gamebirds and corvids. Some species were recorded but without evidence of breeding behaviour. Results in 1990 showed that the reserve held high densities of breeding songbirds, whereas other parts of the site, mainly sheep grazed grassland interspersed with unmanaged 10-15 year old blocks of mixed trees and shrubs, held considerably fewer species (Table 7.12). A positive correlation was found between pair density and the ratio of shoreline to land area. The St Peter's area (12ha) of the reserve was designed as a series of small inter-connected lagoons with long undulating edges, thus maximising the water edge habitat. There are very few trees over 5m in height in this area but below this the volume of foliage, created by coppicing, is high. A few grassy glades are kept open by mowing. There is thus both good feeding habitat and nesting cover in the reserve.

Only one other area on the site, Arboretum Lake, has similarities in habitat structure to the reserve (long shore-line, relatively high foliage volume, etc.). It has a mature hedge, a broad mix of plant species, and scrub has invaded from the site margins. It can be seen from Table 7.12 that this area held the greatest density of songbirds in the unmanaged part of the site. Elsewhere, even in the ungrazed parts, feeding and nesting habitat quality is low. In the poorer habitats, songbird territories were large and were often confined to the water edges.

Blackhorse Lake provided an extreme contrast to the habitat in the reserve. It is a large, oval lake without islands, which is grazed to its margins and has little emergent aquatic vegetation. In consequence, the area has little value for wildlife and only skylarks were recorded breeding during the CBC.

In 1990 more than half the species breeding in the reserve were residents. Following a run of mild winters, the populations of some resident songbirds (eg wren, long-tailed tit, reed bunting) were high nationally. Wren and reed bunting pair densities in the reserve were 2.1 and 2.2 pairs per hectare respectively. Elsewhere on the site, territory size was greater and pair density was 20 to 25% less. The number of pairs of wrens in the reserve was reduced by around half in 1991. There was a period of severe weather in the preceding February which is assumed to have had a serious effect on this species. Robins also appear to have suffered, whereas reed buntings - which move out of the reserve in winter - survived well.

Five species of warbler regularly breed in the reserve. More sedge warblers hold territories than any other

Good mixed songbird habitat within the reserve.

migrant and they were the most numerous bird in the reserve in 1990 and 1991. Sedge warblers will occupy any dense vegetation at or close to wetland margins and the gradation from aquatic plants through to thick terrestrial cover is ideal for them. The related reed warbler was restricted to the small reed beds in the reserve and was one of the few species which was more numerous on Trout Lake, where there are well developed stands of reed.

The virtual absence of mature trees means hole-nesting species are limited by a lack of nest sites. Stock dove, little owl, green and great spotted woodpecker, great and blue tit all nested just outside the reserve in holes in old willow pollards or stone walls.

The provision of nest boxes will almost certainly increase the number of these birds breeding in the reserve and might attract species, such as redstart and spotted flycatcher, which are only seen on passage at present.

Migrant birds

The reserve area is clearly attractive to migrant birds on passage, and regular mist-netting in the St Peter's area has confirmed this. Netting takes place in spring (April to early June) and autumn (July to mid-October). Particularly significant are the large number of migrant reed-bed and scrub-dwelling warblers caught. In 1990, birds of some species were recaptured often enough to permit an approximate estimate of the total numbers passing through the reserve, using a single-session, mark and recapture method. These estimates demonstrated that spring numbers were well in excess of the breeding populations, as indicated by the CBC. Migrants, especially sedge warblers, evidently passed through in large numbers. In autumn, the importance of the reserve was even more evident, with estimates of 650 sedge warblers, 420 reed warblers, 800 willow warblers, 80 chiffchaffs, 220 blackcaps, 160 garden warblers and 140 lesser whitethroats passing through. Such numbers of birds, together with the less common

Table 7.12. The number of occupied territories of each species of songbird recorded during the CBC in different parts of the Great Linford site in 1990, and in the wildfowl reserve (WR) in 1991.

Species	1990					1991
	Wildfowl Reserve (WR)	Arboretum	Trout	Haul	Blackhorse	WR
Skylark	2	–	2	1	4	3
Wren	21	7	11	7	–	13
Dunnock	4	2		1	–	3
Grasshopper warbler	–	–	–	–	–	1
Sedge warbler	25	2	4	1	–	26
Reed warbler	5	2	9	2	–	4
Garden warbler	3	1	1	–	–	6
Blackcap	1	2	–	–	–	2
Whitethroat	1	2	–	–	–	–
Lesser whitethroat	1	–	1	1	–	1
Willow warbler	10	2	4	2	–	11
Robin	5	4	3	1	–	–
Blackbird	12	6	4	4	–	8
Song thrush	2	2	–	–	–	2
Mistle thrush	–	1	–	–	–	–
Long-tailed tit	2	1	1	1	–	3
Blue tit	2	2	–	1	–	4
Great tit	2	1	–	1	–	3
Reed bunting	22	4	12	5	–	25
Chaffinch	4	4	6	3	–	4
Greenfinch	1	1	1	1	–	4
Goldfinch	1	1	–	–	–	–
Linnet	4	2	–	–	–	4
Bullfinch	2	–	–	1	–	3
No. of species	22	20	14	16	1	19
No. of pairs (minimum)	132	49	59	32	4	130
No. of pairs/ha	12	6	3	4	0.25	12

Table 7.13: Numbers of birds in the reserve in 1990 and 1991.

Species	Spring 90	Spring 91	Autumn 90	Autumn 91	Totals 90	Totals 91
Turtledove	1				1	
Kingfisher	2		4	1	6	1
Great spotted woodpecker			1	1	1	1
Swallow				2		2
Tree pipit				1		1
Wren	8	2	42	26	50	28
Dunnock	8	5	21	11	29	16
Robin	5		20	18	25	18
Redstart			1	1	1	1
Fieldfare				1		1
Blackbird	17	9	19	38	36	47
Song thrush	5	3	4	6	9	9
Redwing		1	1	14	1	15
Sedge warbler	70	8	155	78	225	86
Reed warbler	19	1	147	127	166	128
Grasshopper warbler				1		1
Lesser whitethroat	4	1	49	14	53	15
Whitethroat	2	1	17	8	19	9
Garden warbler	13	2	47	37	60	39
Blackcap	19	10	73	53	92	63
Chiffchaff	0	1	42	3	42	4
Willow warbler	20	10	271	129	291	139
Spotted flycatcher			1	1	1	1
Goldcrest			7		7	
Long-tailed tit	18	9	17	4	35	13
Blue tit	5	4	55	34	60	38
Great tit	8	2	20	11	28	13
Treecreeper			3	3	3	3
Chaffinch	5	1	5	7	10	8
Bullfinch	17	9	15	29	32	38
Greenfinch	9	7	78	32	87	39
Goldfinch	5	2	9	3	14	5
Linnet		1				1
Redpoll	3		2		5	
Reed bunting	18	8	30	26	48	34
Total	281	97	1156	720	1437	817

species, using an area of only 12ha demonstrate the benefits of habitat management.

The number of birds caught in 1990 and 1991 were very different, although trapping effort was similar in the two years (Table 7.13). In 1991 fewer migrants were caught in spring and, following very poor weather in the breeding season, numbers were well down in autumn: These findings at Great Linford mirrored the situation nationally.

Results from mist-netting can therefore indicate the use of the reserve by migrants. This allows reserve management to be assessed as well as showing year to year variation, reflecting wider population changes. As more ringed birds are re-captured at Great Linford and ringers at other sites catch our ringed birds, information is also accumulating on the position of the reserve in the network of places used regularly by migrants in Britain. A duck decoy on the reserve Main Lake would allow ringing of large numbers of waterfowl and would add greatly to the value of the bird ringing studies already carried out. The Wildfowl and Wetlands Trust have recently called for an increase in waterfowl ringing activity.

Mammals

The reserve, buffered by surrounding rough grazing, forms a haven for small mammals, mustelids and brown hares. There is an extremely high population of hares, which contrasts strongly with the numbers on nearby intensively managed farmland. Foxes are common and attempts have been made to control their numbers to reduce predation of nesting wildfowl. Foxes, carrion crows and magpies are the chief predators, together with feral mink. Mink are a serious pest; there is circumstantial evidence that water vole numbers in particular have fallen drastically since their

The Great Linford Coypu: Trapped in the 1970s.

arrival. Mink are now so well established that local efforts to control their numbers can have little effect.

The reserve lies within the territory of at least one group of badgers. A permanent sett has not been established within the reserve but badgers have made use of an old culvert during the summer months. Bats are commonly seen hunting in the reserve and by the river in spring and summer. Three species have been positively identified to date. Mature willow pollards beside the river provide roost sites, whereas there are few suitable holes and splits in the relatively young trees in the reserve as yet. The provision of bat boxes may increase the population.

The final mammalian visitor to the reserve was a single wandering coypu, trapped in the mid-1970s by Roger Tomlinson, ARC's site warden. This coypu record must have been one of the furthest westerly outliers for the species before the MAFF eradication programme sealed their fate in the East Anglian fenland.

Conclusion - habitat management success

The restoration of the worked-out gravel pits at Great Linford, following their designation as a wildfowl refuge, has led to the establishment of a high quality nature reserve. Its increasing attractiveness to both breeding and wintering wildfowl has been matched by an increase in the variety of other wildlife. In 20 years, the reserve area has changed from a relatively sterile post-industrial landscape to a rich and varied wetland habitat. It is one of the best bird-watching sites in the county of Buckinghamshire and is nationally important for several species.

Table 7.14. Mammals

Hedgehog	*Erinaceus europaeus*
Pygmy shrew	*Sorex minutus*
Common shrew	*Sorex araneus*
Water shrew	*Neomys fodiens*
Mole	*Talpa europaea*
Long-eared bat	*Plecotus auritus*
Pipistrelle	*Pipistrellus pipistrellus*
Noctule	*Nyctalus noctula*
Rabbit	*Oryctolagus cuniculus*
Brown hare	*Lepus europaeus*
Bank vole	*Clethrionomys glareolus*
Water vole	*Arvicola amphibus*
Short-tailed field vole	*Microtus agrestis*
Wood mouse	*Apodemus sylvaticus*
Brown rat	*Rattus norvegicus*
House mouse	*Mus musculus*
Red fox	*Vulpes vulpes*
Badger	*Meles meles*
Stoat	*Mustela erminea*
Weasel	*Mustela nivalis*
American mink	*Mustela vison*
Muntjac	*Muntiacus reevesi*
Coypu	*Myocastor coypus*

CHAPTER 8

SUCCESSES OF THE PROJECT

The work conducted jointly by ARC and The Game Conservancy on the gravel pits at Great Linford over the last twenty years has been unique. When it began, industrial sponsorship for environmental projects was almost unknown. In recent years many companies have sought to green their image by short-term financial involvement with conservation. But ecology is a long-term science and occasional injections of cash can do little to solve its mysteries and safeguard the environment.

The ARC contribution at Great Linford has been sustained over an unprecedented period and in financial terms has totalled well over one million pounds at 1992 prices. The extent of this backing for ecological research on man-made wetlands is unique.

Project achievements

The reclamation of the post-industrial landscape of the Great Linford gravel pits has been both rapid and complete. By applying restoration techniques derived from the forefront of ecological thinking, ARC and The Game Conservancy have provided a blueprint for the generation of high quality nature reserves from worked out gravel pits. Both organisations recognise that not all exhausted mineral workings can become nature reserves, but the lessons learned at Great Linford now enable an efficient transition to a diverse wildlife habitat wherever that is the desired after use.

Coincidental with our research at Great Linford has been a colossal growth in the leisure industry and the development of completely new water-based sports such as windsurfing and still-water trout angling. Work at Great Linford has shed light on the inter-relationship between these and wildlife conservation and has helped ARC and other companies to resolve the potential conflicts between them. The practical experience of developing the Great Linford reserve has also provided clear insights into the management of

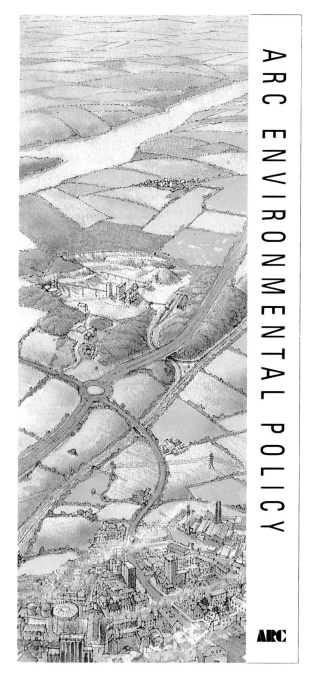

ARC ENVIRONMENTAL POLICY

ARC

ARC's Environmental Policy commitments have been amply met over the 20 years of cooperation at the Great Linford Wildfowl Centre.

A message from the Chairman of The Game Conservancy . . .

Game 2000 is a statement of the aims, objectives and policies of The Game Conservancy. It includes notes on the importance of game conservation and the implications of The Game Conservancy's policy for game management, and it provides guidelines for the development of The Game Conservancy to the year 2000.

I believe that all those who shoot game should, in their own interests, take heed of Game 2000 and work with The Game Conservancy towards the objectives outlined within it. Our maxim must always be **conservation through wise use.**

SIR CHARLES MORRISON MP
JUNE 1989

Through the research at Great Linford, The Game Conservancy has progressed towards the objectives outlined in its manifesto *"Game 2000"*.

the public at nature reserves. The interests of bird watchers and naturalists are not always sympathetic to nature conservation itself but with careful management of reserve walkways, hides and viewing points, the needs of both can be met. In short, the project at Great Linford has advanced immeasurably the certainty with which those who are planning the after use of mineral workings can operate.

The Great Linford research in the wider context of freshwater ecology.

The research conducted at Linford has provided useful scientific information on at least three levels: basic

ecological data; interactions between species; and community ecology processes. These are described briefly in the following paragraphs.

The basic ecological data from the project includes prescriptions for landform profiles and the use of differing soil types and planting patterns to produce varied botanical communities. Also in this category fall the data on duckling and fish diets and on the breeding ecology of ducks and geese.

The work has established a wide variety of important relationships between species. The major conclusion from the work is that *competition* in the strictest population ecology sense, (ie, having a two-way effect on the population biology of two or more species) appears to have been demonstrated under field conditions. Competition is easy to produce in laboratory experiments but is very difficult to demonstrate under natural conditions. The particular example of competition which we have demonstrated is that between tufted (and probably mallard) ducklings and coarse fish (bream, tench and perch) in their use of invertebrates as a food source.

Suppression, in the population ecology sense (ie. a one-way negative effect on the biology of one or more species) was also demonstrated. Submerged aquatic plant growth was suppressed by bream and roach. This was limiting the usage of Main Lake by wintering herbivorous waterfowl (gadwall, mute swan, coot) to very low numbers. Subsequent to the fish-removal the peak numbers of all three species increased markedly on Main Lake compared with those counted on an adjacent control lake.

Two fundamental concepts in population ecology, *competition* and *suppression* have therefore been illustrated by the research at Great Linford.

Freshwater ecologists often argue whether the productivity of aquatic ecosystems is limited principally by 'top-down' or 'bottom-up' factors. Top-down factors include predation and competition for limited food and

space. Bottom-up factors include sunlight and nutrient availability for decomposition and primary production processes which can then fuel the upper links in the food chain. The Linford work has demonstrated that, in the relatively simple ecosystems of gravel pits, top-down influences (predation by fish on invertebrates, competition with ducks for food, and suppression of submerged water plants) play a vital role in controlling invertebrate and plant productivity. Controlled experimental work in ponds supported this conclusion by demonstrating that these changes were not simply year to year variations in plant and invertebrate abundance, but were due to the actions of the fish.

Benefits to ARC

The cooperation between ARC and The Game Conservancy throughout the project has been so close that it is almost impossible to divide the benefits between the organisations. Inevitably, however, there are some results which will be of more use in the future to the aggregates industry and others which are of longer term benefit to conservation.

In the former category, the earlier experimental work at Great Linford with the landforms of post-industrial gravel pits was crucial. When the project began we simply did not know what the best shapes, bank profiles, island structures and water level control programmes would be. At the conclusion of the project ARC and others can reshape disused gravel workings into nature reserves on the basis of scientifically proven results.

Furthermore, we now know much more about the ongoing management of nature reserves which have been formed from gravel pits. We know how to manipulate the aquatic vegetation through the regulation of fish populations; we know how best to manage the coppice and scrub which springs up around the margins of the lakes; and we know how to manipulate the water levels to encourage weed growth, invertebrates and wading birds. Whilst the precise management inputs will vary from site to site, sufficient has been learned at Great Linford to allow ecologists to supply a management prescription for any typical gravel pit restoration programme.

ARC, through its long involvement with the project, has demonstrated in a very tangible way the terms of its corporate environmental policy:

"Our aim is to strike an appropriate balance between meeting the nation's need for construction materials and our desire to protect the natural environment."

Benefits to The Game Conservancy

At the outset of the project, The Game Conservancy was hopeful that research at Great Linford would resolve the question of poor duck breeding performance on man-made wetlands. Quite early on in the research it became apparent that the three key factors were the provision of nesting habitat, the control of predation, and in particular the availability of invertebrates as food for the growing ducklings. However, it was only the long-term nature of the research that enabled us to investigate and resolve the question of the inter-relationship between fish and ducks. That work in turn led us down avenues of research which we had no conception would be studied at Great Linford when the project was begun. Such is the nature of the questions that ecology continually poses.

Our studies of pike and tench have broken new ground. We have added to the general understanding of the interaction between coarse fish, water weed, invertebrates and wildfowl. The research on invertebrates in particular has been taken to such a degree of detail that we are now able to model on computer the likely effects of any manipulation of fish populations on the invertebrate communities of any restored gravel pit ecosystem.

The development of the reserve has attracted more and more species, not only of waterfowl, but of wading birds, plants, mammals and invertebrates. We were able to study the features of the reserve which attracted particular plant and animal species. This in turn has led to research on the interactions between them. The day to day management of a nature reserve which has, in effect, been a living laboratory has necessitated our becoming experts on everything from the ecology of water snails to little ringed plover; of willow trees to the rare and declining spined loach.

The Game Conservancy's primary objectives, set out in its manifesto *"Game 2000"*, are that the populations of game, wildfowl and fish should be conserved at densities which allow careful cropping and that such conservation should be regarded as a valid use of sustainable managed resources. In many ways the research at Great Linford has enhanced the achievement of these objectives and has stimulated our understanding of the management of other game and wildlife populations far removed from the man-made wetlands on which this particular avenue of research took place.

Benefits to the wider public

The results of the research conducted over twenty years at Great Linford have been publicly available throughout the project and the publication of this final report in particular will serve to disseminate them to a much wider audience. Any conservationist, any mineral company, any Government department or any enthusiastic individual can make maximum use of the lessons which we have learned. There has been no attempt to suppress or retain information for commercial or academic advantage. The results of the project and its implications for the management of man-made wetlands are there for all, and for all time.

Finally, of course, there is the reserve at Great Linford itself. This book provides ample evidence that the Great Linford Wildfowl Centre is now something very special; not only within the county of Buckinghamshire but of national conservation significance. It will continue to develop and we have no doubt that the diversity of the species found there will continue to increase. Whatever the future of the development of the Great Linford area, the future of the Wildfowl Centre itself will be secure. It will not simply be a monument to a research project which once came and went. It will instead be a living testimony to the research which has been conducted in and around the lakes of the site and of the value of a close and ongoing cooperation between industry and environmental science.

APPENDIX 1

Scientific Papers Published During The Research At Great Linford

Barnard S. [1989] Simulation modelling the gravel pit ecosystem *Game Conservancy Annual Review* 20, 1988, 150-151.

Barnard S. [1990] Modelling species interactions in a gravel pit lake. *Game Conservancy Annual Review* 21, 1989, 113-114.

Barnard S. [1991] Modelling the Canada Goose populations at Great Linford. *Game Conservancy Annual Review*, 22, 1990.

Birkhead M. [1983] Lead poisoning and Wildfowl; the results of two separate studies. *Game Conservancy Annual Review* 14, 1982, 78-81.

Birkhead M.[1984] Mallard: what makes a good egg? *Game Conservancy Annual Review*, 15, 1983, 35-36.

Birkhead M.[1985] Variations in the egg quality and composition in the mallard *Anas platyrhynchos. Ibis*, 127, 467-475.

England J. [1990] The importance of alderfly (*Sialis lutaria*) predation on chironomids. *Game Conservancy Annual Review*, 21, 1989, 115.

Giles N. [1987] Population biology of the Three-spined Sticklebacks, (*Gasterosteus aculeatus*) in Scotland. *J.Zool. Lond.* 212, 255-265.

Giles N. [1987] A comparison of the behavioural responses of parasitised and non-parasitised Three-spined Sticklebacks (*Gasterosteus aculeatus L.*) to progressive hypoxia. *J. Fish Biol.*, 30, 631-638.

Giles N. [1987] Predation risk and reduced foraging activity in fish:- experiments with parasitised and non-parasitised Three-spined Sticklebacks, (*Gasterosteus aculeatus L.*) *J. Fish Biol.* 31, 37-44.

Giles N. [1987] Differences in the ecology of wet-dug and dry dug gravel pit lakes. *Game Conservancy Annual Review*, 18, 1986, 130-133.

Giles N. [1988] Native brown trout in decline. *Game Conservancy Annual Review*, 19, 1987, 145-147.

Giles N. [1989] Tufted ducklings benefit from increased invertebrate food abundance. *Game Conservancy Annual Review*, 20, 1988, 141-142.

Giles N. [1989] Assessing the status of British wild brown trout stocks (*Salmo trutta*): a pilot study utilizing data from game fisheries. *Freshwater Biology*, 21, 125-133. Special issue on: Wild brown trout: the scientific basis for their conservation and management (ed J.M. Elliott).

Giles N. [1989] Experiments on substrate choice and feeding efficiency of downy tufted ducklings *Aythya fuligula. Wildfowl*, 40, 74-79.

Giles N. [1989] Tufted ducks on gravel pits...a success story. *New Scientist* 25, 42.

Giles N. [1990] Progress in brown trout research. *Game Conservancy Annual Review*, 21, 1989, 120-121. (includes questionnaire).

Giles N. [1990] Effects of increasing larval chironomid densities on the underwater feeding success of downy tufted ducklings, *Aythya fuligula. Wildfowl*, 41, 99-106.

Giles N. [1990] Improvement of wetland habitat for wildfowl by removal of fish. *Proceedings of IWRB/EPA Sweden International workshop on Wetland Management and restoration*, Lake Hornborga Sweden.

Giles N. [1991] Wild trout research project.The Connemara Sea Trout Collapse. *Game Conservancy Annual Review*, 22, 1990, 135-137.

Giles N. [1991] Gravel Pit Restoration for Wildlife (ed J. Andrews & D.J. Kinsman). RSPB. 1. Diving ducks Page. 72. 2. Fish communities. Pages 56-58.

Giles. N [1991] Tufted duck habitat use and brood survival increases after fish-removal. In: *Aquatic Birds in the trophic web of lakes, Symposium on the Ecology of Aquatic Birds*. University of Mount Allison, New Brunswick, Candada.

Giles N. [1992] Status of wild trout populations in the British Isles. In: *"Freshwater Quality"*, the 16th Report of The Royal Commission on Environmental Pollution. Ed Prof J.H. Lawton.

Giles, N. [1992] A review of the status of wild trout populations in the British Isles. *Game Conservancy Annual Review* 23.

Giles N. & Pehrsson 0. [in press] Ecological interactions between fish and waterfowl. International Waterfowl and Wetlands Research Bureau, Training manual.

Giles N. & Street M. [1990] Management of the Great Linford Canada and Greylag geese populations 1972 -1989. *BASC Symposium on Management of Canada Geese in Britain.* Nov 1989.

Giles N. & Street M. [1990] Management of the feral Greylag and Canada goose flocks at Great Linford. *Game Conservancy Annual Review* 21, 1989, 116-117.

Giles N. & Traill-Stevenson A. [1990] Recent changes in habitat use by broods of tufted ducks. *Game Conservancy Annual Review* 21, 1989, 111-112.

Giles N. & Wright R.M. [1987] Reproductive success of Canada and Greylag geese on gravel pits. *Game Conservancy Annual Review* 18, 1986, 142-145.

Giles N., Phillips V. & Barnard S. [1990] The Current Crisis: Ecological effects of low-flows in chalk streams. *Royal Society for Nature Conservation* 1991.

Giles N., Phillips, V. & Barnard, S. [1992] Ecological Effects of Low Flows in Chalk Streams. *Game Conservancy Annual Review* 23.

Giles N., Street M. & Wright R.M. [1987] Feeding overlap between fish and waterfowl on gravel pit lakes. *Game Conservancy Annual Review*, 18, 1986, 134-38.

Giles N., Street M. & Wright R.M. [1988] Potential competition for food between fish and ducklings on gravel pit lakes. *Game Conservancy Annual Review*, 19, 1987, 135-138.

Giles N., Street M. & Wright R.M. [1990] Diet composition prey and preference of tench *Tinca tinca L.*, common bream *Abramis brama L.*, perch *Perca fluviatilis L.* and roach *Rutilius rutilis L.* in two contrasting gravel pit lakes: potential trophic overlap with wildfowl. *J. Fish Biology*, 37, 945-957.

Giles N., Tucker C. & Traill-Stevenson A. [1988] Habitat use by tufted duckling broods. *Game Conservancy Annual Review* 19, 1987, 153-155.

Giles N., Wright R.M. & Nord E.M. [1986] Cannibalism in Pike fry, *Esox lucius L.*: some experiments with fry densities. *Journal of Fish Biology*, 29, 107-113.

Giles N., Street M., Wright R.M. & Traill-Stevenson A.J. [1992] A 5-year study of the effects of fish on the food supply for waterfowl in gravel pit lakes. *In prep.*

Giles N., Street M., Wright R.M. & Traill-Stevenson A.J. [1992] Fish reduce invertebrate abundance in experimental ponds. *In prep.*

Giles N., Street M., Wright R.M., Phillips V. & Traill-Stevenson A. [1989] Food for wildfowl increases after fish removal. *Game Conservancy Annual Review* 20, 1988, 137-141.

Giles N., Street M., Wright R.M., Philliips V. & Traill-Stevenson A. [1991] A review of the fish and duck research at Great Linford 1986-1990. *Game Conservancy Annual Review*, 22, 1991, 129-133.

Gray N. [1974] The ARC Wildfowl project. *Game Conservancy Annual Review*, 5, 1973, 20-32.

Halewood J. [1988] Insect emergence on the gravel pits of a wildfowl reserve. *Game Conservancy Annual Review*, 19, 1987, 139-140.

Haywood S. [1988] The breeding biology of Canada and Greylag geese at Great Linford. *Game Conservancy Annual Review*, 20, 1990, 148-150.

Hill D.A. [1980] A new study on ducks *Game Conservancy Annual Review*, 11 1979, 39-41.

Hill D.A. [1981] Nest predation in mallard and tufted duck. *Game Conservancy Annual Review*, 12, 1980, 94-97.

Hill D.A. [1982] Importance of duckling survival. *Game Conservancy Annual Review*, 13, 1981, 94-101.

Hill D.A. [1983] Compensatory mortality in the mallard. *Game Conservancy Annual Review*, 14, 1982, 87-92.

Hill D.A. [1983] Habitat requirements of breeding waterfowl on gravel quarries: management implications. *Proc. Symposium on Man-made Wetlands.* Great Linford 1983.

Hill D.A. [1984] Population regulation in the mallard *Anas platyrhynchos L. J. Animal Ecol.* 53, 192-202.

Hill D.A. [1984] Factors affecting nest success in the mallard and tufted duck. *Ornis Scand.* 15, 115-122.

Hill D.A. [1984] Laying date, clutch size and egg size of the mallard, *Anas platyrynchos* and tufted duck *Aythya fuligula. Ibis*, 126, 484-495.

Hill D.A. [1984] Clutch predation in relation to nest density in mallard and tufted duck. *Wildfowl*, 35, 151-156.

Hill D.A. & Ellis N. [1984] Survival and age related changes in the foraging behaviour of tufted ducklings, *Aythya fuligula. Ibis*, 126, 544-550.

Hill D.A., Wright R.M. & Street M. [1986] Survival of mallard ducklings *Anas platyrynchos* and competition with fish for invertebrates on a flooded gravel quarry in England. *Ibis*, 129, 159-167.

Lees P.R. & Street M. [1973] The Amey Roadstone Wildfowl Project. *Game Conservancy Annual Review*, 4, 1972, 27-33. Annual report on the year's research and activities.

Lees P.R. & Street M. [1973] The feeding ecology of young mallard *Anas platyrynchos L.* and tufted duck *Athya fuligula L.* in wet gravel quarries. *Proc. XII Congr. I.U.G.B. Stockholm, Sweden*, 249-253.

Phillips V. & Traill-Stevenson A. [1989] Wildfowl respond to changes in a gravel pit lake following fish removal. *Game Conservancy Annual Review*, 20, 1990, 143-144.

Phillips V. [1990] Selective feeding behaviour by pochard at Great Linford, in winter. *Game Conservancy Annual Review*, 21, 1990, 102-104.

Phillips V. [1991] Pochard *Aythya ferina* use of chironomid rich feeding habitat in winter. *Bird Study*, 38,

Phillips, V. [1992] Variation in winter wildfowl numbers on gravel pit lakes at Great Linford, Buckinghamshire, 1974-79 and 1984-91, with particular reference to the effects of fish removal. *Bird Study*.

Phillips V. & Phillips J. [1991] Habitat management for nesting wildfowl benefits songbird populations. *Game Conservancy Annual Review*, 22, 1990, 142-145.

Street M. [1975] Seasonal changes in diet, body weight and condition of fledged mallard (*Anas platyrynchos L.*) in eastern England. *Proc. XIII Congr. I.U.G.B.*, Lisbon, 339-347.

Street M. [1975] The Amey Roadstone/Game Conservancy Wildfowl Project. *Game Conservancy Annual Review*, 6, 1974, 28-32.

Street M. [1976] The Amey Roadstone/Game Conservancy Wildfowl Project. *Game Conservancy Annual Review*, 7, 1975, 55-60.

Street M. [1977] The food of mallard ducklings in a wet gravel quarry and its relation to duckling survival. *Wildfowl*, 28, 113-125.

Street M. [1977] The Amey Roadstone Wildfowl Project; 1976. *Game Conservancy Annual Review*, 8, 1976, 35-43.

Street M. [1978] The Amey Roadstone/Game Conservancy Wildfowl Project. *Game Conservancy Annual Review*, 9, 1977, 49-59.

Street M. [1978] The role of insects in the diet of mallard ducklings; an experimental approach. *Wildfowl*, 29.

Street M. [1979] Research on the improvement of gravel pits for waterfowl by adding straw. *Game Conservancy Annual Review*, 10, 1978, 56-61.

Street M. [1979] The management of artificial wetlands for waterfowl: a novel technique to increase the availability of invertebrate food organisms. *Proc. XIV Congr. I.U.G.B.*, Dublin, 159-174.

Street M. [1980] The importance of invertebrates and straw. *Game Conservancy Annual Review*, 11, 1979, 34-38.

Street M. [1981] The assessment of mortality resulting from the ingestion of spent lead shot by mallard wintering in south-east England. *Proc. XV Congr. I.U.G.B.*, Trujillo, Spain.

Street M. [1981] Mortality in the mallard and the role of poisoning by spent lead shot. *Game Conservancy Annual Review*, 12, 1980, 89-93.

Street M. [1982] Some ways of reducing ingestion of lead shot. *Game Conservancy Annual Review*, 13 1981, 101.

Street M. [1982] Research at Great Linford and wildfowl management. *Game Conservancy Annual Review*, 13, 1981 91-94.

Street M. [1983] The Great Linford Wildfowl Project a case history. *Proc. Symp. Wildlife on man made Wetlands*, Wildfowl Centre, 1983.

Street M. [1983] The use of straw to promote the production of invertebrate foods for waterfowl. Chapter 10 in *Managing Wetlands and their birds*, IWRB, Slimbridge.

Street M. [1985] The restoration of gravel pits for wildfowl. A practical handbook. pub. by ARC Public affairs Dept., ARC Ltd., The Ridge, Chipping Sodbury, Bristol.

Street M. [1986] Water levels and wading birds. *Game Conservancy Annual Review*, 17 1985, 114-117.

Street M. [1986] Industrial homes for waterfowl. *Birdwatchers Year Book and Diary*. Buckingham Press.

Street M. [1988] The comparative importance of islands and predator control for increasing waterfowl nest success. *Game Conservancy Annual Review*, 19, 1987, 148-152.

Street M. [1989] Ponds and lakes for waterfowl. *Game Conservancy Green Advisory Guide*, 3.

Street M. [1990] The effects of water manipulation on habitat use by duck broods. *Game Conservancy Annual Review*, 21, 1989, 118-119.

Street M. & Titmus G. [1979] The colonisation of experimental ponds by Chironomidae (*Diptera*). Aquatic Insects, 1, 4, 233-244

Street M. & Titmus G. [1981] A field experiment on the value of allochthonous straw as food and cover for lake macro-invertebrates. *Freshwater Biology*, 12, 5, 403-410.

Street M. & Wright R.M. [1983] Do growing goslings need invertebrates as part of their diet? *Game Conservancy Annual Review*, 14, 1982, 82-86.

Street M. & Wright R.M. [1984] 1. The diet of goslings 2. Do fish compete with waterfowl for food? *Game Conservancy Annual Review*, 15, 1983, 31-33.

Titmus G. [1979] The emergence of midges (*Diptera:Chironomidae*) from a wet gravel pit. *Freshwater Biol.*, 9, 165-179.

Titmus G. & Badcock R.M. [1981] Distribution and feeding of larval chironomids in a gravel pit lake. *J. Fish Biol.*, 11, 263-271.

Traill Stevenson A. [1988] Agricultural damage by geese. *Game Conservancy Annual Review*, 19, 1989, 155-156.

Wright R.M. & Street M. [1985] The influence of fish on survival of wildfowl broods. *Game Conservancy Annual Review*, 16, 1984, 77-80.

Wright R.M. [1986] The role of pike in a wildfowl reserve. *Game Conservancy Annual Review*, 17, 1985, 118-120.

Wright R.M. [1987] The pike populations of the ARC Wildfowl reserve. *Game Conservancy Annual Review*, 18, 1986, 139-141.

Wright R.M. [1988] Pike population dynamics. *Game Conservancy Annual Review*, 19, 1987, 141-144.

Wright R.M. [1989] Prey selection and food consumption of pike in two gravel pit lakes. *Game Conservancy Annual Review*, 20, 1988, 145-147.

Wright R.M.[1989] Bream populations and the effects of fish removal on aquatic vegetation. *Game Conservancy Annual Review*, 21, 1989, 109-110.

Wright R.M.[1990] Aspects of the ecology of bream *Abramis brama* L. in a gravel pit lake and the effects of reducing the population density. *J. Fish Biol.* 37, 629-634.

Wright R. M. [1990] The population biology of pike *Esox lucius* L. in two gravel pit lakes, with special reference to early life history. *J. Fish Biol.*, 36, 215-229.

Wright R.M. & Giles N. [1987] The survival, growth and diet of pike fry (*Esox lucius* L.) stocked at different densities in experimental ponds. *J. of Fish Biol.*, 30, 617-629.

Wright R.M. & Giles N. [1988] Breeding success of Canada and Greylag geese (*Branta canadensis and Anser anser*) on gravel pits. *Bird Study*, 35, 31-36.

Wright R.M. & Giles N. [1991] The population biology of tench, *Tinca tinca L.* in two gravel pit lakes. *J. Fish Biol.*, 38, 17-28.

Wright R.M. & Phillips V.E. [1990] Mallard duckling response to increased food supply in the wildfowl reserve. *Game Conservancy Annual Review*, 21, 1989, 105-108.

Wright R.M. & Phillips V.E. [1991] Reducing the breeding success of Canada and Greylag geese. *Game Conservancy Annual Review*, 22, 1990, 138-140.

Wright R.M. & Phillips V.E. [in press] Reducing the breeding success of Canada and Greylag geese, (*Branta canadensis and Anser anser*) on gravel pit lakes. *Wildfowl.*

Wright R.M. & Phillips V.E. [in press] Changes in aquatic vegetation of two gravel pit lakes after reducing the fish population density. *Aquatic Botany.*

Wright R.M. & Shoesmith E.A. [1988] The reproductive success of pike, Esox lucius L.; aspects of fecundity, egg density and survival. *J. Fish Biol.*, 33, 623-636.

Wright R.M. & White G. [1986] The population biology and distribution of pike (*Esox lucius L.*) as determined by ultrasonic tracking in an artificial reservoir. *Proc. 3rd Freshwater Fisheries Conf., Liverpool.*

APPENDIX 2

Additional References Cited In The Text

Andrews, J. &. Kinsman, D. [1990] Gravel pit restoration for wildlife – a practical manual. RSPB, Sandy, UK.

Byrd, V. G. & Woolington, D. W. [1983] Ecology of Aleutian Canada Geese at Buldir Island, Alaska. US Dept. Interior Fish Wildlife Service Sci. Rep. 253.c.

Craven, S. R., Bartlett, A. G., Rusch, D. H. & Trost, R. E., [1985] Distribution and movement of Canada Geese in response to management changes in East Central Wisconsin, 1975-1981. Wisconsin Dept. Nat. Resources Tech. Bull. 158, Madison, Wisconsin.

Downing, G. [1991] The landowner's viewpoint. In Harradine J. (Ed.) Canada Geese – problems and management needs. Proc. BASC Seminar, Marford Mill UK 1989.

Fabricius, E. [1983] Kanadagasen i Sverige. Baturvardverket Rapport 1678.

Feare, C. [1991] Control measures and their effectiveness. In Harradine J. (Ed.) Canada Geese – problems and management needs. Proc. BASC Seminar, Marford Mill UK 1989.

Fox, A. D. & Mitchell, C. R. [1988] Migration and seasonal distribution of Gadwall from Britain and Ireland: a preliminary assessment. *Wildfowl* **39:** 145-152.

Fox, A. D. [1991] The Gadwall in Britain. *British Wildlife* **3:** 63-70.

Fuller, R. J. [1982] Bird habitats in Britain. T. A. & D. Poyser, Calton, UK.

Giles, N. [1990] Canada's menacing export. Country Life, April 12th, 1990 p96-97.

Harradine, J. [1991] Canada Geese and shooting. In Harradine J. (Ed.) Canada Geese – problems and management needs. Proc. BASC Seminar, Marford Mill, UK 1989.

Klopman, R. B. [1958] The nesting of the Canada Goose at Bog Lake, Manitoba. Wilson Bull. 70, 168-183.

Lessells, C. M. [1986] Brood size in Canada Geese: a manipulation experiment. J.Anim.Ecol., 55, 669-689.

Madsen, J. & Andersson, A. [1990] Status and management of *Bratana canadensis* in Europe. In.

Matthews G. V. T. (Ed.) [1989] Managing waterfowl populations. Proc. IWRB Symp., Astrakhan 1989. IWRB Spec. Publ. 12, Slimbridge, UK.

Milne, B. S. [1974] Ecological Succession and Bird-life at a Newly Excavated Gravel-pit. *Bird Study* **21:** 263-279.

Monval, J-Y. & Pirot, J-Y. [1989] Results of the IWRB International Waterfowl Census 1967-1986. *IWRB Special Publication No. 8.* Slimbridge, Gloucester GL2 7BX.

Ogilvie, M. A. [1977] The numbers of Canada Geese in Britain, 1976. Wildfowl 28, 27034.

Owen, M. & Salmon, D. G. [1989] Federal Greylag Geese *Anser anser* in Britain and Ireland, 1960-1986. Bird Study 35, 37-45.

Owen, M. [1977] Wildfowl in Europe. Macmillan, London.

Owen, M. [1991] The Canada Goose: its ecology and behaviour. In Harradine J. (Ed.) Canada Geese – problems and management needs. Proc. BASC Seminar, Marford Mill, UK 1989.

Owen, M. Atkinson-Willes, G. L. & Salmon, D. G. [1986] *WIldfowl in Great Britain.* Cambridge University Press.

Piersma, T. [1986] Breeding waders in Europe. A review of population size and a bibliography of information sources. Wader Study Group Bull. **48:** Suppl.

Salmon, D. G. [1991] Numbers and trends of Canada Geese in Britain 1960-2000. In Harradine J. (Ed.) Canada Geese – problems and management needs. Proc. BASC Seminar, Marford Mill, UK 1989.

Simpson, W. J. [1991] Agricultral damage and its prevention. In Harradine J. (Ed.) Canada Geese – problems and management needs. Proc. BASC Seminar, Milford Mill, UK 1989.

Tuite, C. H. [1982] The Impact of Water-based Recration on the Waterfowl of Enclosed Inland Waters in Britain. *Report to the Sports Council and the Nature Conservancy Council.*

Walker, A. F. G, [1970] The moult migration of Yorkshire Canada Geese. Wildfowl 21, 99-104.

Watmough, B. [1983] The effects of recreation on waterfowl. Unpubl. *Rep. to the Sports Council/Nature Conservancy Council.*